'I should have done this a long time ago. People tell me I look younger and more relaxed and I feel more cheerful. I was amazed at how quickly I changed after a few sessions. Better posture has helped me feel really, really good.' Karen Levine, events organiser

'The Alexander Technique is my secret weapon in maintaining calm when my hectic lifestyle gets out of control. The improvement in focus and concentration has been a real boost to my work.' Melissa Burrows, banker

'I sailed through my pregnancy with barely a twinge thanks to Noël's work with me on the Alexander Technique over the last couple of years – despite the fact that I had always had back problems in the past.' Mohini Chandra, artist

'I have acquired a new, open posture that has given me new energy flows, new attitude and new horizons I did not experience before.' Dr Martin Rosenberg, management consultant

'Having Alexander lessons with Noël has helped my voice become clearer and more resonant. I also feel more comfortable when speaking in public.' Ronald Davis, marketing consultant

'I feel taller, my breathing is easier, and also being looser helps me maintain my balance in those awful winter winds which previously threatened to blow me over. Now I feel stronger, I hope to be able to carry on for a few more years.' Ella Scotchmer, 103 years old

'I have been amazed at the improvement in my back pain after just nine sessions. You seem to apply no pressure at all, yet I really do begin to feel taller. My wife says my posture has improved, which is the ultimate compliment!' Keki Dadiseth, Divisional Director, Unilever

'I didn't realise my bad posture had affected my ability to deal with business clients, but my confidence has grown immensely with the Alexander Technique.'   Sebastian Boon, financial adviser

The Alexander Technique helps both your body and your mind to work more efficiently. After a lesson with Noël, I think more clearly, communicate more effectively and generally feel calmer and more on top of things. I glide through the day both physically and metaphorically.'   Karen Wheeler, journalist

'Noël really helped me while writing my book – crouched all day over my computer I was getting shoulder pains and my posture was collapsed. The sessions with Noël were a lifesaver – I would open up and lengthen and widen to my full stature. Now I'm able to maintain it for myself.'   Sahar Hashemi, entrepreneur

The effects of the Alexander Technique have been immediate, long-lasting and very positive! From my first appointment, I could feel the muscles in my neck loosen and relax, and I now know how to effect this change for myself. The days of having a stiff, cramped neck are consigned to history!'   Theresa Corry, banker

'Knocking three strokes off my golf handicap by improving my posture has surprised every one of my opponents. I now play a full round without backache the following day.'   Harry Scott, property agent

'Improving my posture has transformed my physical wellbeing. Forty years of neck and back tension has disappeared.'   Stephen Pollard, political commentator

'I never thought I would be able to pick up my twins without pain in my back. I can't believe how improving my posture has made playtime with my kids much more fun.'   Stephen Burdge, Managing Director, film design agency

'My improved posture and co-ordination has helped me overcome my nervousness. I feel a lot more confident and outgoing. I like myself better.'   Pamela Russell

'Improving my posture has really helped my running. I can run faster and for longer without my knees hurting.'   Richard Brodie, designer

'Since having Alexander lessons for only three weeks I was able to stand at a music concert for four hours with no back pain at all, something which I have not been able to do for five years. I feel fantastic.'   Kelly Edge, secretary

'I only regret that I was not taught much earlier in life how beneficial the simple expedient of 'non-doing' and following the straightforward instructions of an Alexander teacher could be to my health and well-being. I have since made up for lost time!'   Andrew Pinnell, solicitor

'The Alexander Technique gave me a new lease of life; almost overnight I felt liberated and strangely vertical.'   Stephen Hyett, solicitor

'My husband noticed with pleasure I was developing a much better defined waist; a result of the Alexander lessons I was having with Noël Kingsley.'   Susan Crowther, author

'Some years ago I was diagnosed with a lung condition and my specialist suggested that the Alexander Technique might be of help to expand my lung capacity. I have been having one-to-one lessons and I can now breathe more deeply and my lung capacity has increased. It is the best thing I did. I now stand taller, my legs are stronger and I no longer feel hesitant in crossing roads or walking down stairs. I have a more positive attitude to life and feel calmer in dealing with situations.'   Audrey Oliver

'I stand taller, my shoulders are wider and I feel bigger – without any effort.'   Jimmy Chan, investment analyst

'During my second pregnancy I suffered from quite severe sciatica. Having had various treatments without success, I decided to visit Noël Kingsley. Within a few months the pain had completely subsided and I felt like a new person. During my third pregnancy I regularly saw Noël Kingsley and the sciatica did not return – and has not since.'   Dr Caroline Fertleman, paediatric registrar

'I became interested in learning about the Alexander Technique in order to improve posture with the final objective of reducing lower back and neck pain, but as I progressed through the classes I found the technique also useful in improving my overall level of aware- ness both physically and emotionally.'   Delfin Rueda, Vice President, leading global investment bank

'I work in restoration but it took me a while to apply it to myself . . . It's liberating to cast away bad postural habits and learn, even later in life, that it's possible to grow and stand up for yourself in a relaxed and rejuvenating way. I have learned to stand tall again and move well both on dry land and in the water . . . and to be free of pain. Good posture enhances life!'   Colin Amery, writer and archi- tectural consultant

'Learning to free my neck, facial muscles and jaw has really helped me articulate more successfully than any number of tongue-twisters. Also, improving my posture and being free of old habits has extended the range of roles I can play.' Catherine Hemming, actress

Perfect Poise, Perfect Life

Bring Your Body into Balance and Revolutionise Your Life

NOËL KINGSLEY

HODDER

MOBIUS

First published in Great Britain in 2005 by Hodder and Stoughton
A division of Hodder Headline

This paperback edition published in 2006

A Mobius paperback

1

A CIP catalogue record for this title is
available from the British Library

ISBN 0 340 83580 X

Typeset in 11.5/15.5pt Electra by Palimpsest Book Production Limited,
Polmont, Stirlingshire

Printed and bound by
Clays Ltd, St Ives plc

Hodder Headline's policy is to use papers that are natural, renewable
and recyclable products and made from wood grown in sustainable
forests. The logging and manufacturing processes are expected to
conform to the environmental regulations of the country of origin

Hodder and Stoughton Ltd
A division of Hodder Headline
338 Euston Road
London NW1 3BH

To my parents

DISCLAIMER

All content within *Perfect Poise, Perfect Life* is provided for general information only, and should not be treated as a substitute for the medical advice of your own doctor or any other health care professional. The author is not responsible or liable for any diagnosis made by a user based on the content of *Perfect Poise, Perfect Life*. The author is also not liable in any way to anyone using the guidance, exercises or suggestions or 'helpful tips' or any other information contained in this book. Always consult your own GP if you are in any way concerned about your health.

While the author believes that all information included in this book is accurate and true, he does not accept responsibility, accountability or liability for any inaccuracy.

ACKNOWLEDGEMENTS

I wish to pay tribute to F.M. Alexander, the originator of the Alexander Technique, the method that I have used to my own benefit throughout my whole adult life. It would not have been possible for me to write this book without the experience I have gained as a teacher of the Alexander Technique.

I also wish to convey a special thanks to Walter Carrington, a protégé and colleague of Alexander himself for twenty years and his wife Dilys Carrington, both founding directors of the Constructive Teaching Centre, London. I owe them a deep debt of gratitude. I also wish to thank Marjory Barlow, the late Peggy Williams, as well as Jeanne Day and her late husband Aksel Haahr who both gave me my first Alexander lessons in 1972. Thank you also to all the other Alexander teachers and students who I have had the benefit of working with, but who are too numerous to mention by name. Thank you also to Rita Hopkins and everyone at Harcourt Clinic, London for their support, and also Dr David Hefferon for his practical help and wisdom.

I would like to acknowledge the thousands of people with whom I have had the pleasure and experience of working, and particularly those who have kindly allowed me to use their cases as examples, and whose names have been changed to protect their identity. Thank you also to those clients who have kindly given testimonials.

ACKNOWLEDGEMENTS

A special thank you goes to my partner Miranda for her love and understanding, advice and encouragement, not only during the time of writing but pretty much all the time for that matter, and for simply being great and looking after me. Also to Glynn MacDonald, Susan Lund, Stephen Pollard, Carrie Boyes, Robert Razz, Jochen Radke, Ronald Harris, Dr Caroline Fertleman and Nancy Brady, who have all assisted me with this book in one way or another. A big hug to all the wonderful people at Insight Seminars and the Essence Foundation for the help and support they have given me over the years. Many grateful thanks go to my wonderful agent Sheila Ableman for all her tremendous experience, advice, strength and enthusiasm and for holding my hand so firmly through the whole process. Thank you also to Rowena Webb, Jacqui Lewis and all at Hodder and Stoughton, my publishers, for their hard work, skill, creativity and professionalism in making this book a reality. Thanks too to copyeditor Morag Lyall.

Last but not least, I would like to thank my father for his love, enthusiastic encouragement and continuing help. I am very grateful to both he and my late mother for introducing me to the Alexander Technique in 1972. By doing so they made it possible for me to help myself make the most of my own life.

Contents

Introduction

You may have come to this book hoping that it may help you be more elegant, beautiful, dynamic, confident, successful, healthy, social, happy, rich, charismatic, athletic and powerful: all perfectly good and understandable reasons, because we want to make the most of ourselves. We want to feel good, and that is what this book is all about.

It's generally accepted that if we want to excel at something we should practise that particular activity to hone our skills. If we want to play tennis better, we are expected to practise our game. If we want to be sexier, then we may adorn ourselves with beautiful clothes. If we want to get promotion and earn more money we expect to work harder. If we want to speak in public effectively, we must practise public speaking. This is all fine as far as it goes. But to every task we undertake we bring the person we are, warts and all, habits and complexes, stoops and hunches, and it's no surprise that we don't achieve everything we hope to or look the way we'd like, even though we may feel that we're applying ourselves 100 per cent. However, it is possible for us to rid ourselves of the harmful habits that hold us back, so that we can achieve what we want more naturally and with less effort. This book will show how you can make the most of yourself.

It's probably true that most of us would like to change something about ourselves. We would like to achieve our full potential and excel in sport, business, public speaking, or simply improve our posture, health and self-confidence. We want to enjoy our life to the full. But so many of us fail to fulfil our dreams, no matter how hard we try, which is what has prompted me to write this book.

Maximising our potential and health ultimately requires us to refine our natural poise, balance and co-ordination. Without such refinement it is not possible for body and mind to function efficiently. This book is intended to offer some insight and awareness into the causes of many problems and how they can be avoided. I also hope to show that not only can we improve, but the possible changes can be extraordinary – for all of us. By bringing your body into balance you can revolutionise your life.

The observations I make are drawn from my experience as a practitioner of the Alexander Technique, a method I have used for over thirty-two years and which has enabled me to achieve more, to be healthy and fulfilled throughout adulthood. I run a full-time practice in central London where I have had the opportunity and pleasure of meeting and working with thousands of people from all walks of life. I chose to change my career in the mid eighties, having had success as a senior executive in a large, national retail organisation. I relinquished the lifestyle I had previously enjoyed to retrain as an Alexander Technique teacher because I wanted to work with the method that had changed my own life and to help people realise their full potential. Every day I work with people who want to change or improve something in their life, be it their health, their abilities in a chosen field, their self-confidence, their voice, or simply their posture. And even now, it never ceases to excite me to see so many make dramatic improvements to their situation and enhance their sense of wellbeing.

The quality we all need in order to function well physically can be described as one of being free, expansive and in balance, all at the same time. Improving our poise does not require any special aptitude or ability. Good poise is our birthright and not only do we all have the instinct for this from birth, we have the inbuilt physical mechanism to cope.

All healthy children experience and enjoy the benefits of natural poise free from any acquired habit. You can regain this wonderful quality by using the Alexander Technique. By doing so you will become more aware of the poor physical habits you've developed since childhood and you can over-come them. This technique gives you a way of becoming more consciously in control so you can begin to rid yourself of your old habits so they cease to affect you. But this book is not about just one technique. It is about life. It is about doing what we want to do, what we've dreamed of doing, and doing it to our best ability.

Perfection itself is elusive. However, by becoming more aware of how we perform our activities it is possible to avoid causing postural and tensional habits that may limit our abilities, so allowing us to function at our best. And while perfect poise itself cannot necessarily guarantee that we will have a perfect life, it's probably true to say that a perfect life cannot be achieved if our poise is less than ideal. Indeed, by improving our poise so that we are free of the habits that hamper us, we are attending to the functioning of our whole body, and that in turn can bring about many positive changes, such as improving our health and reaching wonderful achievements that we wouldn't previously have thought possible.

But we're not dealing with just posture. The manner in which we 'hold ourselves' and do things affects the way our body functions. As with any piece of equipment, if it is not used appropriately there will be unnecessary wear and tear that will ultimately affect the way it functions. As humans we are all susceptible to picking up bad postural habits, and these can cause unnecessary deterioration and affect our efficiency and performance. Our habits are so engrained that we are probably unaware of most of them, yet they characterise everything we do; no matter what task or occupation we undertake, our performance will be influenced by them.

Our physical and mental tendencies can also influence how we feel about ourselves and how we relate and interact with others. Poor postural habits can affect our self-confidence, our speaking voice, our ability to engage fully in social situations, our charisma, our athleticism, dexterity and skill and our elegance. Poor posture can also lead to disabling problems resulting from the years of physical strain.

Incidentally, I prefer to use the word poise rather than posture when describing the ideal situation, because posture implies a rather held and stiff position. Poise on the other hand implies more a quality of balance with the possibility of movement that better relates to how our children are and how we should still be. This may seem too subtle or pedantic, but

I believe it's relevant to our perception of what is required.

I take you through many different life situations in this book, and show how you can improve your health and wellbeing, and better your abilities and performance. But in the majority of cases the approach to making improvements will be an indirect one, by attending to the functioning of your whole body rather than to any specific symptom or activity. By working towards perfection and by applying yourself to the way you do things rather than the end result, you are likely to achieve more than you would by simply trying harder in your habitual manner.

No matter how hard we try to do things well and achieve our full potential, we will find ourselves falling short of our ideals as long as we continue to limit ourselves, albeit unwittingly, by our postural habits. By eliminating these tendencies we are releasing a brake that holds us back; we are likely to find ourselves succeeding where once we failed, being happier and more content, and managing to achieve far more with a lot less effort.

How this book can help you

I have included many real-life examples of how people in different situations have enhanced their professional and social life, confidence, physical abilities, appearance and sense of wellbeing: all by following the principles outlined in these pages. This book will show you where some of your problems and limiting tendencies originate, and also how you can overcome them.

The book is split into three parts. Part One looks at why you may not be functioning at your best, and where the source of your problems may lie. When you read about how your body functions and how our species has evolved, you will see how your habits may be affecting everything you do. Part Two provides lots of helpful tips and suggestions that you can use to make improvements. The principles of the Alexander Technique are outlined in simple terms that you can follow, and there are chapters on how you can be more in control of your body, and how the correct attitude can change your life. Part Three looks at many real-life situations such as performing well at interviews, getting promotion, improving your sporting abilities, being sexy, improving your voice, being naturally confident, and coping with difficult times in your life such as pregnancy, bereavement and divorce.

The exercises that appear throughout the book are more like games or experiments. They do not require you to 'try hard' but rather to use less effort than may be habitual for you. These exercises are fun and are intended to give you a new experience of doing things differently and to help you discover aspects of yourself that you may not have previously noticed. I encourage you to do them and experiment with the 'Helpful Tips'.

You've picked this book up probably because you have a desire to change something about your life, whether you are conscious of it or not. You have dreams and aspirations that are currently not being fulfilled and you may have health and postural problems from which you would like to find freedom. Realising your dreams, fulfilling your potential and enjoying life to the full are what you want to experience. You just need to take the step. Begin by reading this book. Apply these principles that are based on nature and how our bodies are meant to work and you will begin to revive your own natural poise – the poise that nature intended and which is your birthright. Relearn natural poise and you are beginning a process that can revolutionise your life.

Noël Kingsley

Part One
Balance

Part One
Basics

Rediscover Your True Self

1

You're standing there holding this book with a great big grin on your face. You're looking gorgeous, feeling fantastic, healthy and athletic, having enjoyed the morning at the gym, and are quietly confident in the knowledge that you're not only great at sport but a brilliant example to all. You're a success in your field and superb at whatever you turn your hand to. You're beautiful to look at, sex on legs, supple and lithe as a cheetah with the calmness of Buddha in a typhoon and the digestive constitution of a commercial food blender. You are wonderfully co-ordinated, with great breathing, free in all your joints, tall, upright with elegant posture, yet so relaxed and centred you're comfortable within yourself to be humble, confident and fear no criticism. You're great fun to be with, have an equal number of male and female friends and kids just adore you. You are as superb in the boardroom, the kitchen, and at cocktail parties as you are in bed. You don't suffer headaches or back pain and physical stiffness doesn't exist. You succeed at everything you do in love, society, sport, business, public speaking, and enjoy all the little challenges that life throws up. Everything seems to flow your way. In short you are an inspiration to all. If these characteristics apply to you, then you are someone who really doesn't need to read this book. Please pop it back on the shelf and let someone else pick it up. It was wonderful meeting you and congratulations on being so perfect in every way!

If the above does not reflect how you perceive yourself or how you perform, wouldn't you like to be a bit more like that? Would you like a bit more of the cake?

There may be many reasons why you are not achieving your full potential, but there are some reasons that are so fundamental and basic, so easily overlooked that you may be surprised. I'm talking about the habits that all of us may have developed over the years such as poor posture, stiffening our necks, hunching and stooping and generally tensing. These tendencies and hundreds more can have an effect on how well our bodies function and consequently how we perform any given activity. These habits tend to hold us back and prevent us from being as healthy and as successful as we'd like. But if we tackle them head-on, we're likely to find that things change. How would you like to achieve more at everything you apply yourself to? Would you like to be more confident, attractive, successful, healthy, dynamic, calm, upright and more wonderful in every way? Well, I'm pleased to tell you that you probably can.

Many of us feel that we don't match up to our expectations. After all, there are many influences that affect us. 'Modern-day living' is so stressful. We may find it difficult to perform consistently, be it at tennis or at work, or to cope calmly with screaming children at the end of a long day. We may get backache, headaches and stiffness, suffer from shallow breathing, and our posture may leave something to be desired. We may feel uncomfortable within ourselves, lacking confidence, shy of challenges, fearful of speaking in public or making a business presentation. Maybe we're a little clumsy, lose our balance occasionally or get cramps when typing.

Alternatively we may be of an anxious disposition, one who is always shuffling, unsettled, easily irritated and can't sit still for two seconds. We may find it difficult to concentrate, and can never complete a task without jumping to the next, we're always late and forget where we parked the car. Our hips are tight, feet clenched inside our shoes, a bit of a twitch in one eye and we stutter.

Many of us suffer from one problem or another, or we fall short of our expectations. Our sense of wellbeing may not match up to what we expect normal life should offer. But then, what is normal life? Maybe it's normal to be not healthy, and to have problems of posture and general functioning. Can nature be so cruel?

Perfection is a level that not many of us will experience in our lifetime. Indeed, the possibility of reaching such heights of excellence is likely to be beyond anyone's capability. But it is entirely possible for us to make improvements to our health and performance, even to excel beyond our wildest dreams. We may not reach perfection, but none the less we can make big improvements to our lives, to our sense of wellbeing and achieve our full potential.

There are many reasons why we may not be as healthy as we'd like or why we find it hard to function well in today's stressful environment. We may have had an injury or illness that has left us with a handicap or impediment. We may even have had surgery that has left us with physical restrictions and limitations. It's also possible that we have an allergy or intolerance to certain foods that affects our functioning and our emotional moods. These conditions need proper and specialist attention. This book is not dealing with medical illness or sickness that needs treatment from doctors. But, even if we are suffering from one or more of these debilitating situations or conditions, it is likely that life could still be better. How wonderful it would be if we were even just a little bit healthier, more successful and we were able to take everything a bit more in our stride.

Although we may think that we have a number of different problems and fall short of how we would ideally like to be in terms of health and success, it is entirely possible that we are actually closer to what we want than we realise.

If you were to sit down and write a list of your positive attributes, you would probably be able to come up with a short list. I strongly recommend that you do this now as there are some worthwhile benefits. And you may enjoy it! This isn't a time to be modest or shy.

Exercise: Positive attributes

Take a pen and paper and ask yourself what your best characteristics are and what you are good at. This isn't a waste of time, as the longer the list the better will be the benefits. Some of you may find this difficult, but, if pushed, I'm sure you will be able to think of a few. Give yourself a lot of time and make as thorough a list as possible of every positive attribute and good

---

characteristic you have. One hundred won't be too many. (Nice smile, friendly, careful, clear thinking, good legs, thoughtful, patient, loving, generous, etc.) Also list the things you are good at. (Socialising, golf, baking cakes, finding a parking space, texting, technical skills, managing finances, business presentations, making people laugh, sex, etc.) Be honest. It can be an eye-opener for us to see ourselves described with such clarity and you may even be surprised at what you come up with. If you can't think of anything, ask a friend what they think you're good at or what your positive attributes are.

This is really worth doing properly. And see how you feel afterwards. Pretty good, I expect.

But no matter how long your list is, it doesn't stop there. I believe that you are probably more remarkable: you are more talented and have even more positive attributes than you imagine, personally, professionally, socially, in sport or in any activity you undertake. Doubtless you have further qualities that are hidden and as yet lie undiscovered. You're just not aware of them because you haven't yet made the most of yourself.

There is a high chance that the reason why we aren't fulfilling our potential is because we have certain tendencies, habits and personal traits that are preventing us. Are we stopping ourselves from having what we want, and if we ceased holding ourselves back how different could we be? As we move on, we will look at some of these reasons more closely and how we can overcome them.

IN A NUTSHELL

- We are all individual and very different from one another.
- We all have many positive attributes and abilities, some of which are still waiting to be discovered.
- It is likely that we could be much healthier, happier and successful in every way.

How Life Can Throw Us
Off Balance

It is still a commonly held belief that many problems are either physical or mental. For instance poor posture, poor breathing and tension are physical problems, while shyness, timidity, rigid attitudes, lethargy, stress and anger are psychological problems. But in my experience conditions that are so often separated as either mental or physical are completely inter-related and inseparable. Physical tendencies can have an effect on us mentally, and psychological patterns can affect us physically. And our brain controls our body by means of the highly sophisticated communications network of our nervous system, thanks to which we have the potential to function as a wonderfully well-co-ordinated and unified whole person from head to toe. It also means we have the ability consciously to control our behaviour and bodily movements.

Throughout this book I shall be talking mostly from the perspective of how we physically use our bodies to do every-day activities and how this affects our health, our mental outlook and our ability to perform to our ultimate best. This does not discount the effects of our mental condition on our physique, but in my experience I have found that practical changes to our posture and the way we use our body can have far-reaching effects on our whole life. Some things of a very practical nature are so often taken for granted, but need to be addressed in order for us to function well. A better integration of mind and body can influence our emotions, happiness, how we feel about ourselves, and how we relate to others and the outside world. It is from this point of view that we will be considering our situation and making improvements.

We need to make changes to the way we do things because we no longer use our bodies in the way we did as a healthy young child, free of poor postural habits. It is the onset of habits such as stiffening, slouching, and getting off balance that detrimentally affects the way our whole body functions and the way we perform every activity we undertake. I know this from my own personal experience.

I was confronted by my own habits when I was introduced to the Alexander Technique as a young man in 1972. Like all children, I would have been free of postural habits as a toddler, but with so many influences – school, parents, friends – we can quickly fall into habits without realising it. Learning the Alexander Technique by having one-to-one lessons with a teacher helped me to overcome habits that had become engrained during adolescence. I wanted to be free of them as they were influencing my health and hampering my abilities to perform well. Using this technique helped me realise my own full potential and I have continued using it for all my adult life.

By ridding ourselves of these poor postural and physical habits we can make huge changes to our lives. It doesn't matter if we are male or female, young or old, change and improvement are possible, whether professionally, socially, in sport, in our health or whatever activity we undertake. I have seen timid and shy people become more confident, stooped people become more upright, the lethargic become more active and the hyperactive become calmer. Some have gained promotion by their improved stature, calmness and confidence, some have developed their beautiful voice, while others have overcome their health issues and even become pregnant after years without success. The range and scope for change are infinite.

How we are . . . as children

When we're very young we seem to be wonderfully fit and healthy with not a problem or care in the world. We may be a pain in the neck for Mum and Dad, but we're full of beans and of natural good health. We're loose and upright, running, jumping and playing all day long without any pain or discomfort. We're also happy, gregarious and carefree. If you came across a young child who suffered from headaches, a sore back or a stiff neck, you'd think something was seriously wrong. If the infant suffered stress, anger and unusual shyness, again it would appear abnormal. And you'd be right. We don't expect young children to have problems, and if they do we seek expert help.

. . . as adults

We somehow expect adulthood to bring with it physical and psychological problems as part of everyday life. We put it down to getting older, the strains of life taking their toll, the stress of modern society, coping with a temperamental partner, cooking for the children, doing a high-powered and incredibly stressful job, paying the car insurance, school fees, maintaining the house décor, plumbing repairs and fixing the broken lawn-mower. It's no wonder that we get a bit anxious and out of sorts. We may feel that we're losing the edge a bit, and we say, 'I'm getting old!' However, it may be that we're ageing faster than we should, but because so many of us in the western 'civilised' world are suffering in similar ways, we think it's normal.

Staying young

We're still the same human being now that we were at the age of two or three. At one time we were that lively bouncing child, full of joy with not a fear in the world. It's just that we've grown a bit bigger, developed a few wrinkles, lost a few hairs in some places and maybe gained a few more in others; we've matured, at least to some extent, got a few attitudes, habits and responsibilities. We may also have developed some health conditions such as arthritis, but we are essentially still the same person. All our bones and muscles are still in the same place, thank goodness, and they should be doing a similar job to the one they were doing when we were young. Body tissue is being replaced at a similar rate as in a child, and we still heal too, but we do seem to be deteriorating. Should our joints and organs be wearing out quite so quickly? Has nature done such a bad job with us that our working parts break down before the natural end of life? We're very quick to pass off our problems with comments like 'That's life' and 'That's what comes with getting older.' We expect to deteriorate because everyone else does. But life need not be like that. Can we help ourselves to minimise unnecessary deterioration? The simple answer is yes.

If we're suffering from an aching back, stiff neck, tight shoulders or some other similar condition, a doctor will often recommend a painkiller, or some time off work to allow rest. We may be sent for an X-ray to see if there is anything untoward. It is often the case, however, that the ensuing medical report will state that there is some compression of the joints, and the discs are flattened, but no real cause of the pain can be identified. Chiropractors, physiotherapists, osteopaths can all help and the problem or pain may be alleviated for a while, but has the underlying cause been rectified? Many therapies can help treat some symptoms so that we feel more comfortable. But if we have postural tendencies or habits that are with us the whole time, we are likely to revert to the pattern of movement or posture that causes the problem, so we need to keep going back for help.

However, if we take a step back and look at ourselves from a distance, just to see how we appear, we may notice that we have some physical tendencies that may be relevant to the condition in which we find ourselves. It may take some acute observation, but compared to the way that a young child holds herself, is the person in the mirror doing anything different? If we're sufficiently observant, we may notice that we have developed a stoop or some other postural habit such as a tendency to hunch the shoulders. It wouldn't take too big a leap of imagination to realise that our postural condition and habits are not disassociated from our painful symptoms. We may be dealing with a cause and effect.

Poor posture causes problems

There are many ways in which our habitual tendencies can manifest themselves. Obvious symptoms may be pain or discomfort in our back, neck or shoulders, or we may suffer from poor breathing, digestive disorders, high blood pressure or constipation. They also affect the way we feel about ourselves, causing shyness, timidity, lethargy, nervousness and stress. They affect the way we look, how we hold ourselves, and also how we interrelate to others socially and in business.

Consider for example the situation of someone who appears to have a postural stoop. Visualise her standing in front of a group of business executives to whom she's pitching an important marketing proposal, and ask yourself, How does she come across? Her narrowed shoulders and hunch give her a somewhat diminutive stature and she appears insecure and shy. It's highly likely that she is suffering a bit in this way, but manages to muster her courage and do the best she can. But with her diminutive stance, does she present her proposal with strength?

Her husband may also have similar tendencies, and let's imagine him in his new job as public relations director for an international food company. Does his drooped and narrowed posture and shuffling stance inspire confidence in what he's saying? Will he look relaxed and confident when he is required to make a company announcement to the press?

Being aware

Most of us are not aware of the tendencies we have. We develop our postural habits at such an early age, often as young as three or four, that we've been living with them for as long as we can remember. We're not conscious of how we hold ourselves, move, stand, sit or walk. Our habits are almost part of us. Most of the time we are thinking about the hundred and one things we've got to do today, the problem with the bank, how do I get out of this meeting so I have time to buy a new dress for the evening, or watch the rugby final, and how do I finish this report by lunchtime. We don't give any consideration to the body that has to do the job in hand.

We are far more aware of things outside ourselves than what is going on inside us. But here we are, involved in highly complex activities using hundreds of muscles, such as sitting at a desk typing for ten hours a day, and we don't give one thought to how we are doing it. Are we causing unnecessary strain in our forearms and shoulders? Are we hitting the keyboard with fingers like sledgehammers and tightening our wrists excessively? Are we twisted in our chair, with our legs wrapped around each other and the phone squashed between our left shoulder and ear? Are we aware that we haven't breathed for ages? Is it any wonder that we develop physical problems over a period of time?

When we perform repetitive tasks we quickly learn to do them instinctively. If we have bad postural habits they will also affect the manner in which we perform them. Any excessive effort and distortion of our body when performing our activities will become more engrained the longer we continue in this manner, and will eventually cause physical discomfort and excessive wear and tear. We may then suffer from back problems and strained muscles and ligaments that in turn can bring about joint problems, poor breathing and difficulties in concentration, along with many other symptoms.

It is probably true to say that in these days when we perform highly complex and repetitive activities for long periods, we pay no more attention to how we do them, and how we sit, stand and move than our cavemen ancestors did a million years ago. Their daily tasks consisted of more natural and varied activities such as running and hunting, and the speed of change to their lifestyle and type of daily occupations was slow, gradually taking place over thousands of years, keeping pace with their physical evolution. This would have been much slower than the accelerated speed of change in today's modern world.

Blaming other people

Isn't it amazing how ailments just seem to happen to us without our influence or participation? 'The doctor says that the pain in my lower back is because my discs are flattened and squashed and they're pressing on a nerve.' In other words the suggestion is that it's happened to me without any involvement on my part. 'Darling, while I was going to the town centre, a lamppost came out from around a corner and hit our car! I couldn't believe it. Yes, I was driving, but it came out of nowhere!' What I'm saying is that many of us don't accept responsibility, just as though our problems are caused by some divine intervention. It's fate. Or is it? Might it be possible that we have just a little involvement in what is going on inside us?

We don't seem to like taking responsibility for the way we

are, and would much rather place the onus on our doctor, surgeon, chiropractor or the medication to sort us out. It's as though we're passengers on this journey through life and it is completely the responsibility of the specialist, to whom we're often prepared to pay vast sums of money, to fix us. When our condition persists, we blame the specialist and brand them a failure; 'It didn't work.' And when we leave our consultant, we continue to inflict the harm on ourselves with our habits, just as we did when we first entered their consulting room. We can go from one specialist to another in a wide variety of fields in search of the magic solution. And in the end, the answer may simply be that we are causing our own problems through habitual tensions and postural misuse. But this is often too difficult for us to confront and acknowledge.

I believe that our whole person is inseparable: that our mind, body, emotions are all interrelated. And if our overall condition is problematic it is likely to undermine our sense of wellbeing to such a degree that we may be shy, timid, stressed, lacking vital energy, feeling depressed and lethargic. These conditions may feel that they are part of us, but is this really who we are, or are they just symptoms of what we are doing to ourselves?

Could we be closer to health and success than we think? And if so, who or what is stopping us from having them? You as a person are probably pretty well perfect. It's what you are doing to yourself that is imperfect.

IN A NUTSHELL

- We may be causing many of our problems for ourselves.
- If it weren't for our habits, we would be functioning much better and more healthily.
- Unfortunately, most of us are no more aware of how we use our bodies than our cavemen ancestors were a million years ago. Yet in today's world we perform highly complex and repetitive activities compared to their simple tasks.
- If we take responsibility for own condition, we could help ourselves enormously.

Our habits

If I asked the *real* 'you' to stand up, who would you see? If I were to wave a magic wand and transform you into the you without your postural and mental habits, who would you see in the mirror, and who would your friends and colleagues be talking to? Of course, you as a person are right here, holding this book. But is it the same you who held your first colouring-in book at the age of two or three? A lot has changed since then, but genetically you're exactly the same homo sapiens biped. However, you've had many life experiences and probably developed some habits that influence the way you appear, move and think.

Our habits tend to characterise everything we do, affecting our appearance and behaviour. If it were possible to transform you with a magic wand so that you were free of habits in a second, you would probably be amazed. You would be in awe at how fantastic you really are. Wow! If we strip away this hard core of postural habits, restrictive and limiting attitudes that hold you back, you would be nearer to your true self and the way nature intended. And how wonderful you would be!

Habits affect our emotions and character

Physical habits can often have an emotional component that affects how we perceive ourselves and others, how we interact, love, play and work. Stooping, a general collapse of stature and a hollow chest can often be associated with shyness, timidity, as well as depression and lethargy. A tense neck and hunched shoulders and holding the breath often relate to nervousness and stress. Braced backs and rigidly held posture may be connected to anxiety, rigidity of outlook and control. Our physical posture affects our emotional behaviour and feelings and vice versa. An attitude or 'chip on our shoulder' can also make us respond to life's situations in a particular way.

Acquired habits

We don't mean to slouch, or to hunch our shoulders, but we do, and we've been doing it for a long time. Look through a box of old family photographs to see if you can spot a similar trait when you were young. Did you have your postural characteristics, such as a stoop, as a child? In the course of riffling through your faded and discoloured photo memories, you may just find some of your mum and dad, and think how like them you now look, at a similar age. We may be struck by the resemblance, not just of features, but of physical traits. 'Hey, there is the same stoop in Dad that I've now got!' The phrase 'like father, like son', has a foundation in truth. We think that maybe it's genetic, but the fact is also that we tend to copy our parents.

We copy our friends, film stars, pop stars, heroes and heroines too. We learn the same language as our parents and we generally have the same accent because we learn to speak by copying. We learn to tie our shoe laces by copying movement by movement the example of our parents. So if Mum stoops down with a hunched back, stiff shoulders and neck, and she says, 'Look, this is how you tie your shoe laces,' then that is how we will do it! We learn by example and at an amazing speed. The trouble is that our subconscious doesn't separate the good from the bad, and we can develop all sorts of unhelpful habits just as quickly as we learn new skills. It goes to show that we should be careful who we use as an example, but when we're very young we don't have much of a choice.

Parents often ask me what they can do for their children so that they don't develop postural problems. My immediate response is to suggest that they give their children a good example. But since our own postural tendencies became established when we too were very young, we may need to help ourselves before we can help our children.

If we're short-sighted, we know what it's like to be without our glasses or lenses when outdoors. If we're not wearing them, we don't recognise our friends by their facial features, although we notice their height, width and shape, but by the way they hold themselves and the way they move. We have developed these traits by unwittingly copying people of influence. They are not part of us, as such, but things that we do with our bodies.

Our habits work against us

Our habits can have far-reaching effects on our whole body and how we function. For example, a tendency to stoop or slouch can affect our digestion and bowel movements. A stiff neck and shoulders can bring about headaches, affect our breathing and cause anxiety, nervousness and lack of concentration. A tendency to lean forwards while walking can be a cause of stiff knees and an aching lower back. Habits of frowning and fixing our facial muscles can convey the wrong impression socially as well as cause stress, headaches, jaw ache, dull skin and poor complexion.

If we have the habit of stiffening our hips when we walk, we will be using excessive effort to overcome the extra resistance. By eliminating these sorts of habits we will help our body function better and avoid developing more serious problems in later life.

These habits will also affect the way we perform our activities. So if we're keen on football, stiffening our hips will also affect the way we kick the ball. A stiff neck and shoulders will affect the way we swing a golf club or tennis racquet. Tight wrists, fingers and arms will influence the pianist's or violinist's playing to the point where they will never make it to the concert platform. The collapsed chest and tight ribs will never allow the singer to become the success she so desperately wants to be because she can't breathe sufficiently well or produce that elusive beautiful sound.

Sensory awareness

Most importantly, habits have the effect of reducing the sensitivity of our senses. Our sensory perception becomes dulled and inaccurate so that we no longer know what is happening to the degree we should. As an experiment, let's play a game.

Exercise: Sensory awareness – placing feet

How accurate is your self-awareness?

Stand up and close your eyes. Put your hand on something to steady yourself if you need to. Without opening your eyes, place your feet exactly 6 inches apart and parallel like railway lines. Take your time and do it as accurately as you can, without looking. Now open your eyes and look where you have placed them. Are they parallel? Are they where you thought they were? I've done this game with hundreds of people in group classes and it's amazing to see the variations. The space has ranged anywhere from 3 to 12 inches and the feet are often splayed out at quite an angle. This may show some inaccuracy in our sensory perception.

Similarly, we may not sense precisely the degree of tension or effort that is appropriate for the task in hand, so we often misjudge the situation. We may therefore make more effort to do something than is necessary, so our movements become erratic and a little clumsy. For instance, how much tension do you use to hold a pencil when writing? Do your knuckles go white? Could you use less tension? The pencil weighs only a few grams and it isn't going to run away! By relaxing your fingers and hand you will reduce the strain, and benefit your whole arm, shoulder and neck. Since our postural habits are with us every day of our lives, we're probably not really aware of how much effort and tension we're using.

Even if our habits cause us pain, they are familiar, and we humans like familiarity. Indeed we can feel comfortable in our habits and become very attached to them despite the discomfort. But they're not doing us any good and they also undermine our potential performance in anything we do. Consequently we will never achieve our best, no matter how hard we try or how many hours we work or whoever we pay to coach us, because our habits continue to get in the way.

A good friend of mine called Jochen was studying to become a professional musical conductor. Brought up in East Germany, he believed that better opportunities were to be found in the West, so he took the difficult decision to leave his country before the Berlin Wall came down and made his way to West Germany. Earlier, as an adolescent, he had suffered from Scheuermann's Disease which afflicted him in the most severe way by softening and misshaping the vertebrae in his lower spine to the extent that they could not support him normally. This resulted in the surrounding muscles going into spasm in an attempt to keep him upright when his spine wasn't able to do the job, and he endured intense discomfort, pain and depression.

As he grew out of adolescence, his vertebrae solidified in their distorted shape, as is typical for the disease. The muscles, however, did not release their spasm because this pattern of tension had become an established habit. So although the disease was no longer with him, he suffered from extreme back-ache for a further decade to such a degree that he could not stand on the conductor's podium for more than fifteen minutes without it becoming unbearable. The condition was threatening his career.

Of course he had no idea that he was using his muscles in such a way, but it had become a habit during his illness that he had not been aware of, so was unable to rid himself of the tendency without help. During sessions with me he learned how to release the tensions in his back and rediscover his natural poise. His whole co-ordination improved and his back muscles began to function normally again. As a result the back pain disappeared and has never returned.

As Jochen's posture improved so did his ability to conduct. He became more upright, more accurate in his movements and far more commanding in front of an orchestra. His ability to do his job was enhanced by eliminating his harmful postural tendencies.

Time engrains habits

Unless we do something about our habits, our tendencies will increase as we get older, because we are practising them all the time. We become exceptionally good at our habits very quickly, and when we get to the age of sixty or eighty we are just a more exaggerated version of the way we were when we were younger. The only thing that is stopping us from getting rid of these habits is ourselves. We are self-limiting.

But it's never too late to change. I have worked with many elderly people who have found that even in their mature years they are able to improve their health, mobility and enjoyment of life.

Right- and left-handedness

Most of us grow up using one hand more than the other and we become left-handed or right-handed. We make the preference quite early on in childhood without thinking about it when we find it easier to hold an object in one or the other. We subsequently learn to write with that hand, carry, brush our teeth, stir a drink, and a host of other activities with our preferred hand. As a result, we become stronger on that side as the muscles are being used far more than on the other side. Usually there are no problems related to this. However, if our 'sidedness' becomes extreme, it can lead to muscles throughout the body becoming over-developed on one side in relation to the other and this can cause postural twists, a hump on one side of our back, one shoulder higher than the other, and a tendency to lean to one side putting us off balance. Ideally we should try to be as ambidextrous as possible.

Exercise: Be ambidextrous

Choose an activity that you can do safely without either endangering yourself or others, and carry it out with your less dominant hand. So if you're righthanded, stir your coffee with your left; you may unscrew a jar, iron a shirt, put your shoulder bag

---

on the opposite shoulder, dial the phone with the other hand and hold the telephone to the opposite ear, turn the pages of this book, comb your hair, open the door, pour the kettle, brush your teeth, all with the other hand. You will be able to think of many more activities for yourself.

This little exercise can do two things. We discover the degree to which we feel uncomfortable using the other hand and how one-sided we are. We also start to redress the balance so that we are using both sides more evenly and this will have quite an effect on our symmetry, co-ordination and posture.

The effect of small habits

Even small and seemingly insignificant habits can have long-term effects that may eventually develop into problems. For instance, standing with our hands in our pockets may seem a trivial example, but I've seen people doing this and becoming very rounded and hunched in their shoulders. The 'hands-in-pockets' attitude can encourage a thrusting downwards, consequently shortening their whole stature. The habit of standing or sitting with our head at an angle is a typical mannerism in conversation, but many people can get stuck in this position, with excessive tension down one side of the body tilting or twisting them off balance. This can become so engrained that the person may feel that they are actually upright when it's clear that they are not. They are likely to develop stiffness and pain in their neck and shoulders, an opposite twist in their body, along with back problems in the long term.

It is possible to unlearn bad postural habits by thinking before we act. Simply by choosing to do things in a different way we can reduce the effect of our previous harmful habit, and become more adaptable. Some small changes that can seem unimportant can open up new opportunities and lead to major changes in our lives.

IN A NUTSHELL

- Our habits characterise everything we do, but because we're so accustomed to them they feel natural.
- Poor postural habits are copied and learned from our parents, pop and film stars, friends, and are also caused by stress.
- If we unlearn our habits we may well be amazed at how much better we feel both physically and mentally.

HELPFUL TIPS

1. Notice any habits you have. Do you walk down the street on the same side every day? Do you hunch your shoulder when talking on the phone? Do you pick things up with the same hand? Which shoulder do you carry your shoulder bag on?
2. Choose to do things differently. Perform simple activities with the other hand. This will balance your musculature and reduce one-handedness.

Two Legs to Stand On
3

Please stand up a minute and take the book with you if you like, but stand upright and look down at your feet. Look how far away they are from your head and how small they seem. Take a really good look at them and ponder over your situation for a minute. Here you are, standing on two small platforms that are probably between 6 and 12 inches in length depending on your overall size, and nor are they very wide. However, your height is likely to be at least 5 feet and may well be over 6 feet. It doesn't take much to realise that for such a tall structure, those are pretty small platforms to be standing on. Now add to this idea some additional considerations to do with weight. Where are the heaviest parts of your body? They are high up, of course. Let's take your head for starters. An adult head probably weighs between 10 and 13 pounds depending on our size. This weight, equivalent to about five bags of sugar, is an incredible amount to be carrying around. If you had a shopping bag that weighed this much, you would not hesitate in putting it down at the earliest opportunity.

Body weight

As well as a heavy head, your upper body is extremely heavy, comprising your upper torso and arms that hang from your shoulders. Now, for a moment, I'd like you to imagine that you were a designer working for a human being production company, and they asked you to design a new sort of person that would be very stable and not fall over. Would you design or draw a shape that had the bulk of its weight located towards the top end of an upright structure that was balanced on two small platforms? The answer would probably be, no.

You would probably think that such a structure would be unstable and might topple over. I live in London, and the famous red double-decker buses are vehicles that we see every day. These are designed to have a low centre of gravity, so when one turns a corner, it's able to lean over at an angle of up to 28 degrees without toppling over – something a human can't do! You might say that this is a sensible design. But here you are standing on two little feet at your full height, and you'd be right in thinking that you are a little precarious in design.

You're not only standing, but you're holding this book. It's not a heavy book, but it is additional weight to that of your body. Let's swap the book for a heavy shoulder bag, a baby, a briefcase or laptop, or a box of books, a tray of drinks, or something else that you might want to carry. If you think of the location of your arms and hands that you use to carry things you can see that they too are quite high up. In fact you're adding the weight of your burden to the top half of yourself and it's not too difficult to see that we're becoming even more precarious.

Standing on only two legs

On the surface, it appears that we are really badly designed. Evolution, however, has changed us from four-legged creatures to ones who swung through the trees to the homo sapiens we are now. It's not been a sudden alteration. Change to our physique has evolved slowly over millions of years, but our modern lifestyle does put enormous strain on us. Development from monkeys who walked on hind legs, but used long arms to steady themselves, has taken a very long time. Some people would say that we shouldn't be on two feet at all and we should still be on all fours. Well, the reality of the situation is that we actually are on two feet, so we'd better make the most of it.

However, if we look a little closer, it would appear that we have evolved appropriately to be on two feet. Indeed we have a balancing mechanism that is working away all the time to keep us upright. This balancing mechanism includes our cerebellum in the brain, the suboccipital muscles in the neck and the vestibular mechanism of the inner ear and also our eyes. The vestibular mechanism of our inner ear consists of miniature tubes containing fluid and they act rather like spirit levels. If we move our head then the fluid within the tubes moves against minuscule hairs, which informs our brain of a change in our position in space in relation to gravity. There is some evidence that during our evolution during millions of years the angles of these tubes in our inner ear have rotated around 90 degrees. This has allowed our head to be upright in its current position on our vertical body, rather than stuck out in front of a horizontal body like a horse or other four-legged animal.

Not only do we have a balancing mechanism, but we also have what we could call a postural mechanism consisting of an arrangement of muscles whose function is to keep us upright, without any perceived effort. Muscles in the body mainly fall into two groups. One group of muscles is used for movement such as walking, and the other group exists in order to give us support. These 'support' muscles of the postural mechanism span the joints, keeping us upright at our full height while also allowing us to be expansive in stature. Holding ourselves up and being in balance are not activities that should normally concern us as we have the internal mechanisms to do the job. We just need to make sure that we are not interfering with the systems so that they can work effectively.

Our upper limbs have also adapted by becoming shorter, as they're no longer needed for support, and have become lighter to carry around. The muscle connections from the arms to the body, however, are still well rooted in, so that if we swung through the trees like our cavemen ancestors, or climbed a rock face by pulling ourselves up with our arms, or water-skied, the body doesn't become detached from the arms.

Our hands too have developed so that, along with apes, we enjoy the unique ability of cortical opposition where our thumbs and fingers can close round to make a fist or hold something. This lets us hold a cup of tea or glass of wine.

Benefits of being a biped

There are many benefits of being a biped that encouraged the change from our early quadruped ancestors. Being tall and upright allows us to see into the distance and watch for prey or predators. We can wade through deep water. We can also stretch high up and gather fruit from trees, reach the top kitchen cupboards, or pull ourselves upwards with our arms to climb and save the neighbour's cat that's stuck in a tree. We can use our arms to do things such as carry our children, our harvest of shopping and beer. Now we can stand or sit, and use our upper limbs to do incredibly dexterous activities like writing, typing, manufacturing, playing instruments, games, doing magic tricks or just playing the fool.

Our primitive instincts

A few thousand years ago, our ancient ancestors had extremely primitive lives compared to what we experience now, and their time was mostly taken up with the outdoor physical activities of running, hunting and gathering; an athletic and healthy lifestyle! This way of life existed for hundreds of thousands of years, only slowly changing as we evolved and became more sophisticated.

Eventually our ancestors invented writing, first on blocks of stone, and then eventually on to papyrus or paper. Here we see the birth of the scribe and the beginnings of sitting at a desk or table for hours on end, an activity that's difficult for a biped as we're much better designed for movement than being static. This seems to be the beginning of where man has gone wrong and the accelerating speed of modern development during the recent relatively short period of a few thousand years or so has put even greater strains on us. Here we are, from a postural point of view still relying completely on our primitive instincts, even though the demands of modern living require us to perform increasingly complicated and dextrous tasks.

When we do intricate work such as wiring up electrics, threading needles, typing, working at a desk, performing music, doing artwork, our thoughts are completely on the matter in hand, and it's unlikely that we have any awareness of our bodies at all. We don't give our physical use or posture a thought. It's not surprising that we have problems.

'Trying harder' can be counter-productive

As we push ourselves to perform ever more difficult and intricate tasks, in even less time and under increasing pressures, often because time costs money, we get ourselves into enormous difficulties. The postural habits that we unwittingly picked up as children from Mum, Dad and Uncle Fred have developed and become more pronounced and our tendency towards these habits has become greater with every day that we have practised them. So when we pick up a spoon, pen or spanner or swing the tennis racquet or golf club or play the violin, we're using those same habits of stiffening and tensing, and they generally interfere with our co-ordination. They are with us all the time, affecting and limiting our performance in everything we do. The more we practise them, the less effective we become in our activities. So we try harder, and we usually translate the need to try harder into making more effort still. More effort equals more tension that is likely to upset our co-ordination further. We may eventually get the job done, but at what cost! And so it can be a downward spiral, rather like the helter-skelter at the funfair. The not-so-fun thing is that it's our life that's going that way. If it weren't for our habits, it's likely that we would be able to shine brilliantly at almost everything we do.

Exercise: Writing

There is a lot to consider when writing if we are to eliminate our habits, and more than I can cover with you here. But, as an experiment, I would like you to pick up a pen and paper and sit down at a table. The purpose of the exercise is not necessarily to write very much, but to notice if we are stiffening any part of our body in a way that is not necessary and to experiment with doing it differently.

1. Put the paper on the table and sit down; bring your attention to yourself and your situation.
2. Pick up your pen in your usual way and write something, your name, for instance.
3. Notice how you are sitting.

   Are your feet flat on the floor or are your ankles wrapped around each other or the chair legs?

   Are you sitting evenly on both sitting bones or are you twisted in your seat?

   Are you sitting square to the table?

   Are your shoulders hunched?

   Is your writing hand gripping the pen fiercely or lightly?

   Is your neck dropping forwards and downwards or are you sitting upright?

Experiment with positioning yourself so that you are square to the table and free up so that you are not stiff. Put your feet flat on the floor. Come slightly forwards from your hip joints to lean with a tall back. Hold the pen lightly. Avoid gripping the pen; just let it lie loosely between your fingers. Does this feel unusual compared to the way that you normally hold yourself? You can help yourself enormously by bringing a little awareness to how you perform everyday tasks like this.

IN A NUTSHELL

- **Our bodies have evolved to cope with upright stance over millions of years.**
- **Standing on two feet is precarious. As our centre of gravity is so high, it is essential to ensure that we are in balance so that we can minimise unnecessary strain.**
- **In order to help ourselves, we need to improve our self-awareness and give more attention to how we're performing our activities rather than relying on habit and instinct.**

HELPFUL TIPS

1. Notice if you are stiffening anywhere needlessly and see if you can free yourself of unnecessary tension.
2. Make less effort rather than more when endeavouring to do something well.

Balance and Coping
with Gravity

4

There is one topic of conversation at a party that is pretty well guaranteed to lose our audience within minutes. Nor does it offer the most successful of chat-up lines. Questions such as, 'How are you getting on with gravity these days?' and 'Don't you find gravity so exciting?' are likely to leave us standing alone clutching our drink, wondering if we've got body odour.

However, Newton's discovery is just as relevant to us in this day and age as it has ever been. All those party people who didn't want to hang around while we expounded the virtues of gravitation, and that they're able to sip their Chardonnay from a glass only because gravity keeps it there, may just be missing out on something that could change their lives.

Let's face it, if it wasn't for gravity we wouldn't be sitting here reading this book. And how many millions of people who go to soccer matches or watch them on television are aware that, if it wasn't for gravity, they wouldn't have a game to watch at all, because once the ball was kicked in the air, it wouldn't come back down again? You could say the same about rugby, tennis, basketball, cricket, baseball, American football, tiddlywinks, snooker or even swimming. A pool without water isn't much fun.

Without gravity we just wouldn't have the life we know. It gives us weight and allows us to walk and run. It also gives our internal organs weight so that they hang in the right place suspended by connective tissue from the spine. Gravity aids our digestion, and while we may be able to eat upside down with some difficulty by means of our peristaltic action, it's much easier to eat or drink if our head is higher than our tummy so that it can all flow downwards.

Gravity has helped us to evolve into the design we know, creatures with legs to stand on and heads high enough away from the ground to be able to see into the distance. But, once again, we are reminded of the fact that we're standing on two small feet as bipeds, and being rather tall, with our centre of gravity high up, it makes us quite an unstable structure. This is where we meet the important consideration of balance.

Balance and stability

As gravity gives us weight it's necessary for us to be in balance. This sounds very simplistic and logical, and most of us don't need reminding that things that are not in balance tend to fall over. If a house is leaning as a result of subsidence, engineers prop it up, or strengthen its foundations. If a tree is leaning over too much and we want to save it, we prop it up with supports. If we as people are leaning over, off balance, we also need to do something about it. As it happens, most of us are slightly off balance all the time, but we don't think about it because it's habitual. Our subconscious knows that if we fall over, it hurts, so our body compensates instinctively: we stiffen our muscles and lock our joints.

If you look at the side view of someone who is well-balanced, with free and upright poise – a young child, say – you can draw an imaginary line down from her ear through her shoulder, her hip and down into her ankle. But this ideal state is something that most of us have lost with the onset of postural habits.

We may be able to go through much of our lives being off balance and consequently stiffening our muscles without too much awareness of our problem. But when we're already under strain it may take only a small movement such as lifting our baby off the floor or a box of tools in the garage, and we could injure our backs with the extra effort required to lift the object.

Our balancing mechanism

Balance is something we normally take for granted and don't think of from one day to the next. But if we have been unfortunate enough to experience dizzy spells or an infection in the inner ear, we may recall the alarming sensation of possibly falling over. In the normal situation, however, the balancing mechanism, which includes the inner ear, is working away all the time to ensure that we remain upright.

If we're off balance we'll be stiffening our muscles excessively to compensate and these habits of stiffening will be interfering with the working of our whole body and the efficiency of this delicate balancing mechanism. In order for our bodies to function well it is essential that we do not stiffen our neck or fix our head rigidly in a particular position. Our heavy head needs to balance freely to help our overall balance.

Unnecessary tension not only upsets our muscle co-ordination but also our senses. It upsets everything. It will therefore be impossible for us truly to be aware of our position in space. And unfortunately most adults stiffen their necks nearly all the time.

Holding ourselves stiffly and upright like a soldier so that we don't fall over isn't what life is about. We're not statues or waxworks, we've got a life to get on with! What happens when we want to move? As soon as we do move, our physique needs to adapt constantly to ensure that balance is maintained during the movement, all the time. In other words we need equilibrium: balance while moving. In a healthy situation, our balancing mechanism will attend to this for us as long as we don't interfere with it.

We all have the instinct for survival, and our balancing mechanism responds to our need to live healthily by communicating constantly via the nervous system with the 400 muscles throughout our body. We need it particularly in times of danger. If we trip up, we instinctively stick out a hand to catch ourselves. If we burn our finger on a hot stove, we snatch it away without thinking. In the same way, if we're leaning over off balance, our body is doing something inside to make sure we don't fall. And the response is usually one of stiffening in our ankles, calves, lower back and neck. It may surprise you, but most people when they come to see me on the first occasion are slightly off balance all the time and some people are considerably off balance.

If we are startled by someone slamming the door or a car backfiring, we stiffen. This is called 'startle pattern' and is an instinctive reaction that prepares us for flight. But if we are startled repeatedly or shouted at when we're young, this condition can become a habitual pattern and our stiff neck, hunched shoulders and braced legs become an almost permanent characteristic.

The tendency to be off balance gets worse as we get older simply because gravity is pulling us over all the time and our habits of stiffening become more engrained. So we become more hunched and even stiffer. When we're young, we've got the muscle strength to cope, even if it is causing us posture and health problems and interfering with our co-ordination. When we get older, however, and we don't have the strength to cope with being so off balance, we're given a walking-stick to lean on as an external support. Now we're three-legged! We'll look at this more in chapter 14 about longevity.

If we are off balance, it means that we tend to lean at an angle. This can become even more pronounced if we're doing something stressful such as reporting to our boss or speaking in public.

When we're impatiently waiting in a queue at the bank we may well be leaning forwards, wanting the queue to speed up so that we can get on with our day. If we're required to make a business presentation, it is also more than likely that we are leaning forwards. In our efforts to make a good impression, we come towards those who are listening, anxious to get our point across and to gain approval. But we can see that this puts us off balance. Consequently we'll also be tightening our muscles throughout the body, and probably not breathing very well either. All these tendencies only serve to make us feel more anxious, insecure and nervous than we are already. This throws us further off balance and makes us more tense so our condition gets worse.

Graham came for Alexander Technique sessions because he was suffering from a very stiff back and tired, aching legs. When I asked him to stand upright in the way he would normally, it was clear that he had the tendency to lean forwards at an angle from his ankles so that he wasn't vertical. He had an arched lower back, and the muscles in his back and legs were working overtime just in the effort to keep him standing as he was actually quite off balance. No wonder he was in pain.

As Graham became better balanced his overly tight muscles were able to release some of their tension. Gradually he became more upright, looser, taller and broader. This new way of standing seemed strange to Graham in comparison to what he was used to, but it became more familiar to him as he progressed and his physical awareness improved. He realised that his new stature came not from a stiffly held posture, but from a delicate poise. He was standing in better balance and with a looseness that allowed for easy and free movement. He now no longer stiffens his back and legs in the old way and is free of pain and feels more confidence in himself.

Personal confidence

Although being off balance can be as familiar as an old pair of shoes, our body is constantly under the threat of falling over. The situation excites our fear reflexes so that the necessary tensional compensations are put in place. But we do not feel secure in these circumstances, and nor should we, because if we did, it would show how faulty our sensory perception really is. Being off balance and living with the threat of falling is a situation most of us have been in for a long time and it undermines our general sense of stability, security and confidence.

We cannot feel absolutely confident in ourselves if we're not in balance. If we are put on the spot to meet our future father-in-law for the first time, or walk down the aisle, or challenge our boss, or perform well in sport at the club final, or make an unexpected presentation at work, we can suddenly feel the effects of our limitations. We could compare this to the occasions when we've had a bit of a cold. We can write letters, make phone calls and do most of our day's work without too much of a problem. But if we have to make a speech to a hundred people, we'll almost certainly be wishing that we didn't have this stupid cold because it's undermining our ability to speak and think clearly. Being off balance is a huge influence on our sense of security, and it is right that subconsciously we feel nervous, because we are physically and practically unstable. And being on the back foot, so to speak, is not a good position to perform at our best.

Alisa was in her mid forties when she came for an initial consultation. Although she'd always tried hard to have good posture, she complained of stiffness and of losing her balance and falling over occasionally. She wondered if this could be helped. Although her posture had the semblance of being upright, I could see that she had the tendency to lock herself rather rigidly. During our sessions, I encouraged Alisa to free up and not hold on to the tensions that had become habitual. She gradually became aware of being looser when walking and moving around.

Alisa began to experience the weight of her body going down through her ankles and heels so she became more upright and stable. Her improved looseness allowed her body to compensate better as she moved so that she no longer lost her balance.

Relearning natural poise

If our senses are no longer accurate owing to years of misuse, how can we judge our situation when our system of measurement or assessment is faulty? We become so accustomed to our habits that they feel right but they may be causing us problems. And an improvement to our poise may indeed feel strange and even 'wrong' at first because it doesn't fit with what we perceive as normal or what we think should be 'right'. Anything different from what we're used to will feel unusual. In short, our whole condition needs retraining, probably with the assistance of specialists such as Alexander Technique teachers who can offer the correct guidance and feedback where our own senses are misguiding us.

But all is not lost. Keep breathing! Upright, balanced poise is natural. We have the built-in mechanism to maintain it. We also have the instinct from birth and it can be surprisingly easy to relearn. By improving our balance and co-ordination we will almost certainly achieve more in life.

Exercise: Discover your balance when standing

Perform this exercise to improve your awareness of balance.
First imagine a large wall clock with its pendulum swinging from

---

left to right. Now let's stop the clock. The pendulum will gradually reduce its swing until it stops, pointing downwards. The effect of gravity will ensure that it will be pointing straight down to the centre of the earth.

Now pretend that you are the pendulum. Stand up and place your feet 6 inches apart and pointing forwards. It may be interesting to position yourself side-on to a mirror. Come upright so you're standing tall and try to be relaxed as you do so. Be loose and tall. Now I want you to sway backwards and forwards from your ankles, by a few inches in each direction like a pendulum. Your body should remain upright all the time, so do not bend at the waist or knees. Remain straight. As you sway backwards and forwards try to sense when your body weight passes over the centre. Reduce the sway gradually until the weight of your body is directly over the front of your ankles. You are now likely to be reasonably vertical and probably slightly better balanced. You are not leaning forwards or backwards. Now relax your whole body. You don't need to be stiffening when you're in balance. Experiment like this and find an improved balance as often as you can. Do it anywhere, such as waiting on the station platform, at the bus stop or at home.

Throughout this chapter we have been looking at how it is essential for us to be in balance if we are to avoid stiffening muscles unnecessarily. In the next chapter we are going to consider how this will help us look after the optimum functioning of our whole body.

IN A NUTSHELL

- Gravity is our friend if we're in balance.
- We need to ensure that we're living in harmony with gravity to minimise strain and help ourselves perform well.
- Excess tension and being off balance cause stiffness, poor breathing, nervousness and insecurity.

HELPFUL TIPS

1. Think of freeing up your whole body and particularly your ankles as often as possible.
2. Avoid leaning forwards.
3. Be aware of your balance as often as possible and experiment with finding the centre. Relax your muscles as you do so.
4. Let the whole weight of your body go down through your ankles.

Physical Functioning – A Mechanic's View

Sometimes we need to get down to the nuts and bolts of things to see how they work in order to understand how we should use the equipment; just like a mechanic. We're going to do that here by looking at the physical functioning of our body in simple terms and we'll see how habits can interfere. But let's start with what we can see from the outside.

When we look in the mirror, we are naturally only seeing our external appearance. We may notice that our posture is not ideal, we have a spot on our chin, we need to lose a pound or two in weight and a visit to the hairdresser is overdue. With so much to take our attention, it's easy to forget that there are a million functions going on inside us that we ignore in the whirl of modern-day living. Yet our posture and the way we hold ourselves have an enormous influence on the internal functioning of our body.

Indeed it's a good job that we don't need to think too much about how our internal organs are working as we'd never get anything else done! Fortunately our subconscious takes care of all this, constantly monitoring and controlling our bodily functions. Our heart and lungs circulate a vast amount of fresh oxygenated blood to every cell in our body, while also removing carbon dioxide. The liver and kidneys filter waste products from the blood, and detox our system. Our stomach, large and small intestines process food. Our spleen produces antibodies and protects us against infection. Our nervous system constantly communicates messages from our brain to every part of our body. Then there's our reproductive system, and for a pregnant woman there's a whole lot more going on. We don't need to go into more detail here to get the picture that there's an amazing system working away. So it makes sense to look after it. And while we may remember to drink enough water, avoid junk food, limit our alcohol consumption and get sufficient sleep, we also need to ensure we're not interfering with these functions with bad postural habits.

Looking after ourselves is our responsibility, as there's no one else who can do it for us; and part of this responsibility is to make sure that we give our organs adequate space to function. It doesn't take much thought to realise that if we're slouching and sitting in a generally collapsed manner our internal space will be reduced and will have a squashing effect on all our inner organs.

Exercise: Internal capacity

Sit in a chair and first bring yourself up to your full height as best you can, tall and upright. Then let yourself collapse into a habitual slouch, and you can see easily how your internal capacity has become smaller. What can be large and expansive can also be squashed and compressed. By doing this little exercise our

---

awareness is drawn to the amount of pressure we may put on our insides. We don't have any spare cavities that allow for an overflow if things do get a bit squashed in there. We're full up to capacity. How can our organs possibly work efficiently if they're being cramped and compressed in this manner?

If our internal capacity is compressed, fluids and nutrients can't pass through the system so easily and our bodies become sluggish and less efficient. We will digest less of our food, breathe less efficiently and become more toxic. Consequently we may feel lethargic, depressed, anxious, tired, forgetful, indifferent, heavy and older than our years. If you were stuck on the Underground at rush hour, you wouldn't expect to be able to move, never mind walk down the carriage! Likewise, by slouching and stooping we can create serious problems of congestion and compression inside our bodies.

Exercise: The effect on our emotions

Try another experiment to see how your emotions may be affected by your posture. Put yourself just briefly into an awful slouch, and when you're there, try telling yourself or say aloud with a really big smile, 'I'm happy!' Now bring yourself up to your full height as best you can and say it again: 'I'm happy!' Which way resonates with more truth? Didn't you find it hard to say that you're happy when you were collapsed? And when you said it in an upright poise, didn't it feel more authentic? Now bring yourself into a reasonably upright poise again and say to yourself,

'I'm sad!' That doesn't ring true either, does it? Having good posture helps us feel better.

Our thorax, which is formed by our ribcage, is enormously springy. In fact it is so springy that if someone is unfortunate enough to have open-heart surgery, they are cut down the sternum to allow access for the operation and the ribs simply spring open rather like two cage doors. When the operation is finished, the surgeon has to pull them together in front and staple them closed. If we're misusing ourselves by habits such as tensing and collapsing, we can be compressing this springy structure all the time. Since we develop our habits at a very early age, and if they are severe enough, we can actually squash the shape of our ribcage so that it becomes deformed as it solidifies in adolescence. Sleeping on our front is therefore something to be avoided as this puts pressure on the springiest part of the ribcage.

However, if we learn to change our manner of use and cease to contract our muscles in a harmful way, and if we can come more upright, the ribcage will once again be allowed to expand and create a larger inner cavity for our organs. People having lessons in the Alexander Technique may find that their thoracic capacity increases with the reduction of tension, and some men can find that they increase their chest size by up to 2 inches.

A young lady came to me with poor posture but also complained of acidity and digestive problems. Her life seemed to be a continuous round of social engagements, but her condition made it difficult to participate and enjoy herself fully. After a few sessions, Silvia told me that her problems of acidity had been relieved. She was enjoying a more upright posture and consequently putting less pressure on her digestive organs so food and liquid seemed to be passing through more easily. She is again able to eat the foods and drink her favourite wines that had previously caused her problems.

Ability to twist and turn

The contracting effect of tension in our muscles and the collapse of our backs also compress our joints and cartilage and our whole stature can be shortened considerably. They also affect our flexibility. Our ability to twist, turn and bend becomes dramatically reduced so that such simple movements as looking over our shoulder may not be so easy. The fluid, graceful movements we enjoyed when younger may now seem a distant memory. Do you remember ever doing the hula-hoop?

Wear and tear

Tension in our hips and knees has a similar effect, reducing our ability to walk and run freely. Unnecessary compression in the joints can cause irritation and, as it continues, possibly develop into serious problems. If we continue in this way we may eventually need a hip or knee operation, because we've simply worn the joint away with excessive friction. And we must remember that it is us alone who are creating the friction for ourselves, not some external force. It is you, me and our habits. If we don't stiffen in such a way, then the friction will not be so severe and our bodies are likely to last much longer before they wear out.

One of my clients, Julie, is a very attractive young woman, but she felt that her posture was letting her down, and she wanted to enhance her sense of wellbeing. We made a lot of progress in a few weeks, and then she commented that the improvements were having further benefits beyond her poise. She hadn't mentioned during our initial interview that she suffered from severe disruption to her menstrual cycle and had not menstruated more than twice in the last year. She also suffered from digestive problems. Within weeks of starting her sessions, she reported that her digestion seemed to have improved and a little later she told me that she had resumed normal menstruation. Julie continued to have regular periods.

It's never too late to make a change and improve one's manner of use. Even in later years, we can discover more movement and flexibility than we thought possible. It is really only in very late life, if we've been severely harming ourselves by shortening our stature, that our cartilage discs may be so flattened and dried out that they lose their spring and don't allow movement. But even then it is possible to enhance our sense of wellbeing by addressing our problems of compression. I have worked with many elderly people in their eighties, nineties and even over one hundred, and all have enjoyed an improvement in their poise and health.

Kate was told she had ankylosing spondylitis when she was about thirty, having been misdiagnosed with backache since her early twenties. The disease, which causes inflammation of the vertebral column and chronic stiffness in the surrounding muscle, had given her a dramatic stoop so that the upper half of her torso was bent over at a severe angle. As a result of this stoop, she found it necessary to pull her head backwards considerably just to be able to look ahead. Although the disease had ceased to develop, she had been left with a distortion to her torso that put her severely off balance so her back muscles had been straining just to hold her up, never mind carry her beautiful eighteen-month-old daughter.

Kate had been to many specialists and the most recent conclusions were that her spine was now fused so no movement was possible and nothing more could be done for her. If she needed more painkillers, then they would be provided. She wasn't expected to make any sort of recovery.

During a course of sessions with me, it became clear that there actually was movement in Kate's upper spine, and with the appropriate stimulation from my hands and her own participation in the way I showed her, her back started to straighten up. Although she still has a slight stoop, it is far less pronounced. She has increased her stature, and as a result come into better balance. Now that she is more upright, her back muscles are no longer straining to the same degree and the pain has subsided. Kate now can move around more easily, her breathing has improved and she has more energy. She has also commented that she is less self-conscious of her back in public and feels much more confident. She is thrilled at the change in her appearance. Although Kate still takes an occasional painkiller, it's nowhere near as often, and she hopes to continue making progress and to enjoy an increasingly normal life.

The way we feel and the efficiency of our bodily functions are not only affected by our poise, but also by the manner in which we do things. Simple activities that we take for granted such as carrying objects, holding and working with pieces of equipment can affect us enormously. So we may well not make a connection between some symptoms we're experiencing and a simple activity that we perform regularly.

Patricia is a film director specialising in commercials. She is renowned for her work worldwide and although she benefits from the help of an enormous film crew she prefers to do the actual camera work herself. Patricia works very long hours during the week, and at weekends she would experience severe migraines to the point that physical sickness and an inability to focus were regular occurrences. During her sessions with me, we examined the effects of her tendency to pull her head back dramatically as she looked through the camera viewfinder. We also explored possibilities of holding the camera slightly differently so that there was no need to retract her head to the same degree and she went away to experiment with the new method. Patricia now finds that although she continues to work with a camera for up to ten hours a day, the neck tension has been much reduced and she's been free of migraines ever since. She has continued to have occasional sessions to maintain and make even further progress with her new poise.

I'm not suggesting that poor posture is the reason for all our ailments. If we have internal problems we should always seek the advice of a doctor. We can also receive much beneficial treatment from visiting a specialist such as a qualified homeopath. However, the general functioning of our bodies is affected enormously by the way we hold ourselves, the way we walk, sit, run, hold and carry things. If we reduce our unnecessary tensions and learn to revive our natural poise, we are likely to find that we are more mobile, flexible, athletic, and the inner workings of our bodies will also change, including our circulation, digestion, bowel movements and breathing: all functions that we need to be working 100 per cent if we are to be at our best. Breathing has such an important influence on our whole health and wellbeing that we're going to look at that in more detail. But to summarise what we've covered so far, let's look at the main headlines.

IN A NUTSHELL

- Our bodies have evolved to be expansive.
- Slouching and stooping will reduce the amount of space within our thorax and affect the efficient working of our internal organs.
- These postural habits also affect the way we feel.
- If we can maintain a more upright, loose, expansive poise, we can help the functioning of our whole body including our internal organs.

HELPFUL TIPS

1. Avoid slouching whenever possible to maintain an expansive ribcage.
2. Use the Alexander Technique guidelines in the next chapter to help you.

BREATHING

Do you sometimes think that you forget to breathe? Have you ever found yourself dealing with a difficult problem and suddenly become aware that you have been holding your breath?

Yet the air we breathe, along with adequate food and water are essential fuels for our body. Fortunately for us, however, we normally continue to breathe whether we are asleep in bed, or running a mile. If it was up to us to remember all the time, we probably wouldn't be around to discuss it, have a family, run our business or do anything. We'd all have died off ages ago and our species become extinct. But that hasn't happened because nature has taken care of the situation, and ensured that such vital life functions as breathing and the beating of our heart are automatically controlled for us by our subconscious.

So why is it that we stop breathing occasionally, and in some cases quite often? What has gone wrong? Well, in the majority of cases nothing has gone wrong at all. The respiratory centre in our brain is doing its job efficiently and the lungs are working. However, we cease to breathe momentarily because we simply *hold* our breath. We are in fact stopping ourselves from breathing by tension around the ribcage and diaphragm, by closing the glottis, and tensing in our throat.

Habits and breathing

Although we can hold our breath at times of anxiety, it is extremely common for people to interfere with their breathing all the time. It is as much a habit as any other that we've discussed. But poor breathing isn't just an isolated condition in our bodies. Our breathing mechanism is greatly affected by the working of our body as a whole. Stiffening or tensing anywhere, be it in our legs, arms, neck or back, has the effect of restricting the free flow of air in and out of our lungs. And if we're off balance, as most of us are, we will be tensing throughout, which will consequently affect our breathing too.

Of course, if we have an infection, illness or accident affecting our lungs, then some aspects of our problems may be beyond our control. With any conditions of this nature, the advice and help of a doctor are essential. But aside from these situations, we tend to make things worse by our habits, and poor breathing can often simply be a symptom of 'misuse'. We can be undermining ourselves and our potential by what we're doing to ourselves. It is this aspect that I want to discuss with you: what we are doing, and what we can do to help ourselves.

Oxygen and performance

The ability to think clearly in difficult situations is something that we would all like. We can see the ultimate human performance in Ian Fleming's fictional character, James Bond. Nerves of steel, sheer determination, courage, confidence and pure bravado may be qualities that only a few of us demonstrate. We feel that either we are brave and courageous, or we are not. Although these qualities can be developed by special training, they are also partly the product of a highly co-ordinated system. Oxygen is as much food for the brain as it is for our muscles, and if we're under-breathing or holding our breath, we are certainly undermining ourselves. Once again we come back to our habits, and the need to address them so that we can perform to our full potential.

We need oxygen to feed our muscles. It travels throughout our whole body to every tissue by means of our blood supply, from our scalp to our fingertips and toes. We also need it to feed our brain so that we can think clearly. If we're not breathing properly, we gradually get tired, rather like sitting in a stuffy room with the window closed, but if we open the window and get a bit more air then we become more alert. The oxygen goes to every pore in our body, helping to keep our skin soft and supple, to give us a clear and translucent complexion, shiny hair and white eyes. In other words it can affect how old we look. Breathing well helps us function better, feel more alive and energetic, and look and feel younger.

A closer look

If we look at the situation with the eyes of a mechanic we can see why we make ourselves more stressed. The air we breathe is as much a fuel for our body as petrol is for our car. Without it, we don't function. Breathing is a two-way activity. We need to breathe out in order to breathe in, as you can't breathe in until you've created space for the air. The respiratory centre in our brain is constantly monitoring levels of carbon dioxide, lactic acid and oxygen. We don't want either too much or too little of any of them. Depending on our activity, the respiratory centre will subconsciously stimulate an increase or decrease in the breathing rate to maintain appropriate levels.

Now, we don't need to get too technical here, but a little detail will help to understand why we may feel the way we do in terms of stress, anxiety, confidence, clarity of thinking and energy levels.

Contrary to popular belief, our lungs don't do the breathing. They are only containers that hold and process air. They are like very stretchy bags that expand and contract, and are quite passive in themselves. Located in our back, the two lungs are shaped rather like big fish plates, and extend from the second top rib underneath our shoulder blade down towards the bottom of our ribs. If you put your hand on your middle back, you can feel your clothing, then skin, muscle, your ribs, then your lungs, and in front of them we have other organs.

Our ribs move outwards and inwards by means of our intercostal muscles that span them, and as our lungs adhere to the inside of our ribs they slide and move with them. As the ribs expand, so also do the lungs. Our diaphragm, a muscular sheet rather like a mushroom in shape, divides us in half to create an upper cavity containing the lungs and heart, and a lower cavity with our digestive organs. The diaphragm moves up and down like a piston in the same rhythm as the ribs expand and contract and, between them both, our lungs are encouraged to expand and contract also. As the lungs expand, normal air pressure ensures that there is equal pressure inside us as there is outside, and air is drawn in to fill the increasing space. Similarly, when our ribs contract and our diaphragm moves upwards, squashing our lungs, air is expelled. Any movement you may see in your tummy is simply a displacement caused by the diaphragm compressing your gut on the 'in' breath and releasing the pressure on the 'out' breath.

Your tummy is not directly involved with the breathing process at all. It is worth while mentioning that 'diaphragmatic breathing' is a system that has been developed to help singers and other performers control their breath and voice during performance. We are not discussing that here. We are simply considering what happens with our breathing in normal life situations. But there are some important considerations that explain why healthy breathing is essential for us to perform to our best ability.

When we do something, such as walk to the window to look at the weather, or turn the page of this book, or scratch the tip of our nose, we are using oxygen and glucose to fuel the muscle activity. And rather like our car that produces fumes that need to be got rid of through the exhaust pipe, we create lactic acid and carbon dioxide. While our body needs a small amount of these chemicals to function healthily, we don't want too much. Our body's method of getting rid of the excess is to send it in the bloodstream through our circulatory system of veins, and when it comes to the lungs, the toxins convert into a gas which comes out through our mouth or nose. Our respiratory centre in the brain is constantly monitoring these chemicals to ensure appropriate levels are maintained. This centre also ensures that our rate of breathing is adequate to feed the muscles with oxygen, so that when we exert ourselves it increases, and if we lie down and rest, our breathing slows. This variable rhythm ensures that we are both getting sufficient oxygen and also eliminating the toxins of carbon dioxide and lactic acid to the appropriate levels that our body needs to function healthily. Under normal circumstances, the respiratory centre will look after itself.

If we are not breathing properly, we are likely to be starving ourselves of the fuel we need to function, and also becoming more toxic by not eliminating sufficient chemicals on our 'out' breath. So on the one hand we are deficient in what we need, and on the other have excess of what we don't need. A few people may have the tendency to over-breathe and this is also a symptom of misuse, but is somewhat rarer.

Toxicity and fear

When we hold our breath, we are building up an excess of toxins, particularly lactic acid, above the level that is healthy. An excess of this chemical brings about an undue sense of anxiety, nervousness and fear. If we are interfering with our breathing we can become a little nervous for no apparent reason because we're not aware of holding our breath. This pattern can become so engrained that we can be suffering from nerves all the time, and we just think it's the way we are. We think this is life. If we are then confronted by a stressful situation we tense our muscles and hold our breath even more, creating even more lactic acid. And of course we won't be getting rid of that because we're not breathing adequately, so we will be getting more nervous still. It's a vicious cycle that won't stop until we start breathing again.

The key is to ensure that we are not holding our breath or interfering with the breathing process so that it can regulate itself. We should not *try* to breathe in or breathe out as the trying would still be a sort of interference and involve muscular effort. If you find yourself thinking about something and you suddenly realise that you haven't breathed for ages, start breathing, for goodness sake. Give yourself the oxygen your body so desperately needs and eliminate those toxins. And start by breathing out, so you create the space for fresh air to come in.

But allowing the breathing process to work efficiently involves more than just our lungs. It requires us not to tense our muscles throughout our whole body unnecessarily and to be expansive in posture. And since we're upright bipeds standing tall, it is crucial that we are in balance.

Brian is the author of a number of successful novels. He came to me for reasons of stress and physical discomfort; now in his seventies, he had the feeling that his body was deteriorating. It was clear to me that Brian held himself in a very tense manner throughout his body, and that he held his breath almost constantly. During our sessions when I used my hands to help release his habitual tensions, and as his muscles let go he would suddenly experience a deep breath that would almost surprise him. This tensional release could be in his shoulders, legs, back or neck and the result was an immediate improvement in his breathing. By the end of every session Brian would be much freer, more upright and breathing more freely and deeply. He has continued to make good progress and says that he feels much calmer. He's now able to cope better with stress and be more productive.

In order to improve your breathing, I would encourage you to take the attitude of 'letting the breathing happen'. It shouldn't need any effort and will work beautifully well if you allow it. Indeed, the more you loosen, the better your breathing is likely to become. You can help free up your breathing by performing this simple exercise. Take your time and give a lot of consideration to the preparation.

Exercise: Counting

This simple procedure will help you to breathe more freely.
Preparation:
Stand up and bring yourself upright, but endeavour to do so without stiffening.

Free your neck of unnecessary tension by allowing your nose to drop a little and let your head balance freely at the height between your ears. (This is explained more in chapter 6.)

1. Don't take a special breath for this procedure. Use the air you have in your lungs.
2. Count out loud to five using only one breath. Speak slowly. The words should flow one after the other without a break. If you run out of air, don't force it. Just go up to three or four.
3. When you've finished, allow the air to come into your lungs without sucking or gasping.

---

4. With the new air you have, count up to the next higher number, i.e. six, out loud at the same speed as before.
5. When you've finished, again allow the air to come in without sucking. Let it come in quietly and naturally.
6. Count up to seven this time. Again use only one breath.
7. Continue this procedure up to twelve or as high as is comfortable.

After you have completed this procedure, return to normal breathing. You may find that you are able to reach higher numbers than you might first have expected and that you are breathing more freely and deeply than before.

Robert is often required to communicate campaign plans to the sales and support teams in his role as marketing manager. However, he hates doing it because he finds that he always gets nervous, and long before he even stands up in front of his audience, he is already suffering from symptoms of stress.

He wasn't aware that he tended to lean forwards when presenting, putting himself severely off balance. As a result, he tensed his muscles and this was interfering with his breathing. He therefore found that he couldn't think clearly to remember his opening lines. During sessions with me, Robert gradually became able to maintain a freer neck and shoulders, remain relaxed and upright with his weight over his heels and not to lean forwards. He reduced the interference with his breathing so that he continued to breathe normally when presenting. This has helped his clarity of thinking. He now feels that he can perform his presentations with much less stress, and almost enjoys the opportunity to impress his colleagues in what used to be a terribly daunting situation.

Remember that we don't need to try to breathe because the breathing mechanism will work beautifully well if not interfered with. Your job is to allow it to happen naturally, and if you can, you'll find that your health, happiness and performance in everything you do will improve.

We can help ourselves enormously if we put our minds to it, and better breathing is something that can have a dramatic influence on our whole functioning. But if we are going to help ourselves we need to have a basis to work on and some concrete principles to apply, and we'll be doing all this in Part Two.

IN A NUTSHELL

- Any unnecessary tension in our bodies reduces the efficiency of our breathing mechanism.
- The air we breathe is fuel for our body.
- We need to ensure that we are breathing fully and easily or we shall not be clearing out toxins that can affect our health, confidence and clarity of thinking.
- Breathing will happen automatically if we don't interfere with it.

HELPFUL TIPS

1. Catch yourself out holding your breath and start breathing again!
2. Don't try to control your breathing but just let it happen.
3. Perform the Counting exercise regularly to improve the depth and freedom of your breathing.

Part Two
Improving Your Poise

How Upright Posture Works . . . or Should

Our body has evolved over millions of years to work in a particular way. We have evolved to be upright on two feet, free in all our joints so that we can move easily, and be expansive so that we have the maximum internal space for general functioning such as breathing, digestion, circulation and mobility. If we are habitually tense in unnatural ways, we are compressing our joints and internal capacity so that functioning becomes limited.

We have an instinct for upright poise from birth. As young children between the ages of twelve and sixteen months we've gone through the crawling stage and are getting up on our feet. We have not been taught how to do it, but 'up there' is where it's all happening, so we instinctively come up, to be tall like Mummy and Daddy!

A newborn foal comes out of the womb, lands on the grass all sticky and wet, and instinctively gets up on its feet. It can't even see properly, so it's not copying the example of its mother. The need for survival drives the young foal to stand almost immediately so that it can follow its mother out of danger. Four-legged animals don't have the ability to pick up or carry their young so this instinct has developed out of need for the species to survive.

However, we have the ability to carry our young, rather like monkeys, so we can allow our children to take longer on the ground before they stand up. This slightly slower progress allows our young to spend more time crawling and it's this activity, with the ability to use their hands to play, that has been an important contribution in the development of our brain, hand and eye co-ordination. The rhythmic crawling movements of hands and knees as we move forwards, leading with our heads, has an enormous effect on our nervous system and overall co-ordination and dexterity. In recent years, a link has been established with dyslexia in children who didn't do much crawling when young.

Lead with your head

Coming up tall is instinctive for all children and this influences our co-ordination. In a similar way, four-legged animals want to get up on their feet, and when they move they lead with their head forwards. This seems obvious when we watch a cat as it looks in the direction of a mouse, and decides it wants to play with it. The cat's head carries the eyes and mouth, and it wants its teeth on that mouse! So it sends its head forwards and that action lengthens its spine and tones its back muscles and hindquarters in order to pounce. In other words, it is the need to go forwards with the head that activates its legs to spring or run. The same can be seen in a horse just about to take a jump. It will gallop up towards the fence, and in the last few strides it will gather its hindquarters underneath, and just before it jumps the horse will send its head and

78

neck up and over the fence first, creating an enormous stretch down the back that, in turn, activates its hindquarters. Then it springs off. The head goes forwards first, and the body follows.

We humans are very similar. As infants, we want to get up on to our feet. So we tend to send our head to where we want it, in other words upwards to our highest point. This creates a stretch that activates our back and leg muscles to provide the necessary impulsion for the movement, and the muscle tone to support us. We too lead with our heads. At least we did as infants when crawling and standing. We still need to as adults. However, whereas a child is interested in coming up tall to be closer to Mum and Dad, the things that interest adults tend to be below our eye level – for example computers on desks. This means that we tend to stoop, and collapse in stature.

Since we're not on four legs, our head won't be stuck out in front as other vertebrates, but we do need to lengthen to activate our back and leg muscles. Our head needs to be going in an upward direction similar to the child's in order to create the tone in the musculature that will mobilise and support us. This form of movement is part of a highly sophisticated co-ordination. It doesn't require any perceived effort. Our heads will go upwards because our body's musculature has evolved over millions of years to allow this. Please don't take this idea and start pushing your head upwards, as it will make you stiff. As I said, it doesn't take any effort since it is completely natural. I'll describe how shortly.

Maintaining upright poise

Our bodies are intended to be very springy and expansive in nature. Cartilage between all the joints gives us shock absorption so that the vibrations of running or jumping don't reverberate through our body and rattle our head. The curves in our spine also offer shock absorption, acting like a spring. We all require a quality of looseness and lengthening and widening of our structure to encourage this springiness and to allow our bodies to function efficiently.

If we have the habit of being off balance we will be stiffening lots of muscles unnecessarily. As muscles stiffen, they contract, and this has the effect of shortening and compressing our body. So it's possible that we're not as tall or broad as we should be. Slouching and stooping are other ways in which we compress ourselves. The list of related problems is endless. We get stiff necks, aching backs, inflexibility, poor breathing, digestion and bowel problems, an inability to concentrate, nervousness, lethargy, anxiety and lack of confidence, to name a few.

Being off balance pulls us out of shape, makes us stoop, develop a twist and experience a lot of stiffness. It is also very inefficient, because the effort of moving us around in our daily lives is not being shared proportionately by all the muscles. Just like any good, well-co-ordinated football, hockey or rugby team, all the players need to be in the right place at the right time to pass the ball fluidly towards the opponent's goal. To watch a top team play is like watching a wonderful dance of synchronised teamwork. A poor team, however, may have some good strong players doing all the work, but other lazy players may be standing around not doing their fair share. If the team members aren't all working together, they cannot perform efficiently. It's the same in our body: we need all the muscles to be working together to make light work of moving around.

Some of us manage to maintain a healthy upright poise better than others. We can see this in some of our professional athletes, where their poise helps their co-ordination to reach the extremely high performance levels demanded in their sport. And with this natural poise comes a secure confidence to achieve their objectives. They are lithe, supple in movement, and can be gregarious and expansive in nature. This is a good example of how a healthy, well-balanced physique promotes a healthy outlook on life and vice versa. It's a quality we all need to function well and the instinct in us is there to be rediscovered.

Developing a strong back

Many people feel that their backs aren't strong. In my experience this is often because our back muscles aren't working together properly, i.e. the teamwork of back muscles is not efficient. If we have a weak back the physiotherapist or trainer will often recommend strengthening the tummy muscles to support the back. But we don't see any young children with strong tummy muscles; theirs are soft and relaxed yet they demonstrate the healthiest natural poise in the world. I believe that to develop strong and 'supportive' tummy muscles can cause a lot of harm to our breathing, digestion, bowel movements and reproductive systems. This is because strongly worked muscles can have a shortening and compressing effect on our torso and stature, pulling us down, and restricting the expansive movement of our ribcage. In my experience it is better to improve our posture by improving the co-ordination of our back muscles so that they start to do their job properly without

81

interfering with the tummy muscles. If we encourage the back muscles to work together efficiently to hold us upright in a natural way, they will become stronger to fulfil the task they're being asked to perform. They will strengthen while performing their natural activity more effectively than any gym work that isolates muscles. I have worked with some elderly people who have had stronger backs than many young people who work out regularly in a gym, simply because the muscles in their back are better co-ordinated and working more efficiently.

In the same way as the unco-ordinated football team, our bodies have developed the tendency for some muscles to be working far too hard, getting stiff and wasting energy, while others have been allowed to be a little lazy and not do their fair share. So, for example, some parts of us may be very stiff, such as our neck and shoulders and hips, while our lower back may be rather collapsed and unsupported. But the problem need not be a permanent one. Just like any team, our muscles need good direction and to be retrained.

Muscles need to work together, and are encouraged to do so when a quality of lengthening and widening in stature is restored. We had this as children, and we need it still. With the onset of postural habits from our early childhood we will have lost the instinct to 'lead with our heads' and lengthen in stature. It is therefore easy to see how we may think that lengthening and widening will require some effort. But this is not the case. We have evolved with a particular arrangement of muscles to bring this quality about without any 'perceived' effort. I say perceived, because obviously muscles are working to do the job, but we should not sense it as effort. It's a natural process that will be discussed later in this chapter.

Exercise: Co-ordination

***Let's see how good your co-ordination is by playing
a little game.***

Put the book down for a minute, bring your hands up in front of
your chest and straighten your forefingers so that they are pointing, and line them up to point towards each other, tip to tip. In
a moment I want you to close your eyes and move your hands
away from each other, while still pointing straight forefingers, so
they are as far apart from each other as your shoulders. Then
bring them together so that the tips of your forefingers meet
exactly. Remember to keep your eyes closed. Move them apart
again then bring them together exactly as before. Can you make
them touch accurately each time or do you miss? Now do the
same thing vertically, one fingertip coming downwards towards
the other. Do it repeatedly. Can you also do it diagonally? Can
you do it behind your back? How accurate are you? How is your
co-ordination?

IN A NUTSHELL

- Our postural habits affect our co-ordination and, in
  turn, everything we do.
- All vertebrate animals lead with their heads. As
  humans, our bodies need to work in a similar way.
- Since we are upright, we need to lengthen upwards
  to activate the appropriate muscles for support and
  movement.
- Lengthening in stature happens naturally when the

83

co-ordination is working well and it does not involve any perceived effort.

- In order to function well, we need to be loose, tall, broad and in balance.

HELPFUL TIPS

1. When you get the chance, observe a young child of between two and three years old and watch them balance. They lead with their heads as they come upright, and when they decide to walk they allow their heads to nod slightly forwards to initiate a lengthening of their back and the movement of their legs.

HOW TO HELP YOURSELF

How do we make the most of ourselves? We need to ensure that we're allowing our body to function in the manner in which it's designed. In other words we need to restore the qualities that we all enjoyed as young children before we developed the postural habits that now encumber us.

The Alexander Technique

The person who observed the harmful effects of postural habits and developed a method to overcome them so that we can achieve our full potential was F.M. Alexander, the originator of the Alexander Technique. This is the only method I know of that focuses almost entirely on eliminating our harmful postural habits and reviving our natural poise. Other methods such as Pilates and yoga can be of enormous benefit to us in various ways when we receive good instruction, but in order to rid ourselves of our postural habits and gain more conscious control over ourselves during our daily activities, I must recommend the Alexander Technique. Indeed, it will help you do everything you do in life better. The technique is completely consistent with orthodox medical science.

The Alexander Technique involves us becoming more aware of our balance and we learn to avoid tensing in unhealthy ways and encourage a quality of looseness and expansiveness. We tap into the instinct for good poise that we've had from birth and we utilise our inbuilt balancing and postural mechanisms. So we don't need to be clever and we don't need any special aptitude. We all have the ability to regain the natural poise that is our birthright. The Alexander Technique is a simple method that we can learn to use for ourselves, to be more self-sufficient, to help ourselves be on top form and avoid problems occurring in the future. The technique brings about psycho-physical unity.

This is the method that I have had personal experience of all my adult life, and I would like to share with you now the essential principles and some of the steps you can take to help yourself. It must be said at the outset that it is normal for people to have one-to-one lessons in the Alexander Technique to ensure the fastest progress. I therefore recommend that you find a local practitioner to demonstrate it to you. You may find it a strange and unfamiliar experience, although quite enjoyable – indeed it may even feel wrong according to how you've experienced life up till now. A teacher can help guide you through these stages, reaffirming where you are applying the procedures correctly even if they don't feel right, and so ensure that you are working in the appropriate way to change your manner of use. A teacher will not set out to try to cure you of your symptoms, but will teach you how you can look after yourself on a practical level. As you start to apply these principles, your use of your body is likely to change, which in turn will bring about a natural improvement to your posture and with it an improved co-ordination and an enhanced sense of wellbeing.

I have outlined the main principles of the Alexander Technique here for you. If you follow the guidelines on the following pages you will be giving yourself a big helping hand.

The Principles of the Alexander Technique

In principle it's all very simple. As we've discussed, we are bipeds standing on two feet, and, being upright creatures and living with gravity, it is important that we are in balance. Not only must we be in balance, but free of unnecessary tension. We need to be loose, tall and broad – all at the same time. At first, this sounds like a contradiction in terms because as adults we have come to think that when we're loose, we collapse in a heap on the sofa, and when we want to be tall, we need to try hard to hold ourselves up. But this effort is both unnatural and unsustainable, so we're likely to collapse again; we fluctuate between these two extremes depending on our guilt or fatigue! But life isn't meant to be like that. We're all designed to be upright and free, just as a young child, and how we once were. We still have the capability for it now. The Alexander Technique will help us regain this free and expansive quality that we used to have when we were young.

If we're not in balance we will either fall over or, more likely, we will stiffen our muscles throughout our body to compensate. The extra tension we use to keep ourselves upright despite being off balance can become a habit that will affect everything we do. These tensions interfere with our natural co-ordination so that we don't function efficiently. Using the technique helps us rid ourselves of unwanted habits and regain the natural poise that we need to function at our best. Our body will work perfectly well if we let it. Our job is primarily to stop the harmful things we may be doing to ourselves that are preventing us from functioning efficiently. It therefore requires us to take control of our bodies more consciously. This is achieved by thinking and by bringing our attention to the situation we are in at this present moment. We are constantly being bombarded by various stimuli around us, but in order to help ourselves we need to be able to keep our awareness on ourselves and to apply some conscious control. We will therefore be thinking much more about what we are doing. In this manner we can retrain our muscles to co-ordinate better, a process that will become more instinctive as we progress.

To recap, we want to be loose, tall and broad, well grounded and in balance – all at the same time. This is a big concept to grasp, so in order to regain this natural quality, Alexander broke it down into simple steps. But first we need to be aware of two main aspects of using the technique that will govern how we use the sequence of steps.

The Alexander Technique involves first using a process called 'Inhibition', which is not Freudian in any way, but more a process of preventing the wrong habitual use from occurring. And second we use 'Directions', which are mental instructions to bring about the required freeing up, lengthening and widening. We will use these two main processes to change our co-ordination and improve our poise. We will apply these two processes to the sequence of steps that follow. But first let's look at Inhibition and Direction and some other main principles in more detail.

Inhibition

In order to change, we need to bring our awareness to ourselves so that we can take conscious control and make a decision on *how* we do things. This isn't a hard concentration which may invite stiffening, but an attention that excludes the stimuli around us. We should keep our attention on what we're doing and how we're doing it.

Our habits are all on automatic and will continue to affect us unless we intervene. We need to prevent our habits from kicking in, and also ensure that we *remain* free of our habits. This process is called Inhibition. We can inhibit our habits, and in order to do that we must give ourselves time to think. So the first thing is to *stop*. Give ourselves time. For example, if it is our habit to stiffen our neck every time we pick up the phone, when it rings we could pause for a second to decide to free our neck of unnecessary tension and then keep it free as we pick up the phone.

The principle of Inhibition and its use is fundamental to the Alexander Technique. We should use our ability to prevent wrong use as often as possible. It is the preliminary requirement, before we give our Directions or make a movement. If we inhibit first, we have the opportunity of choosing how we move, or, indeed, whether we move at all. We can give or withhold consent to an action.

It is through the process of Inhibition that we have the ability to ensure that we do not tighten or stiffen unnecessarily. By inhibiting first before acting, we can ensure that we retain our full length and stature, and avoid shortening. Let me re-iterate this as it is so important. If we are going change how we are and how we function, we need to choose, and in order to make a choice we must give ourselves a little time and not rush ahead without thinking. And in order to choose, we must stop first; we must inhibit. It is through using Inhibition that we can change our life.

Direction

Having stopped to give ourselves time to think, we must give appropriate instructions to our body to perform efficiently. This is achieved by thinking, and this process is called 'Directing', or 'giving Directions'. It is sometimes called 'giving Orders'.

We probably all have some muscles working too hard, and others not doing enough. It is virtually impossible for us to identify each of these muscles and, even if we did, we wouldn't be able to control them all individually. Fortunately Alexander discovered that if we think in a certain way, our thoughts can have an effect on our musculature in general without specifying or identifying any particular muscle or muscle group. We learn to think in simple ways that first inhibit our habits, and also bring about an improvement to the co-ordination of our muscles. The improvement to our co-ordination is consistent with the way our body should work, given our evolution. This improvement will give us the support and suppleness and expansiveness we need to function well.

It is important to mention here that 'thinking' is our way of communicating within our body. We communicate through our nervous system from our brain to every part of us, right down to our fingertips and toes. For example, if you decide to pick up a pen your hand and arm will reach out and do it. If you think of walking over to the window to look out, your legs will carry you there. If you think of food for a while, your tummy will start to rumble as digestive juices prepare to receive the food. It doesn't matter what you think of, messages from your brain are going through your body the whole time. And we can use this facility to be more in control.

We're going to deal with things on a more conscious level than we may have previously; our attention will be more on ourselves and how we are doing things. But we need some basis to work on. We need to know *what* to think. This is where Alexander's method comes in. If we *think* of being free of unnecessary tension, we will *become* loose and free. We've just got to think it in the right way. It's not a daydream. This is an instruction in the same way as you would decide to pick up the pen. It's a clear intention, a wish, an internal command. We must *wish*, *want* or *intend* it to happen. We decide how we're going to be then we *let it happen*. But it is absolutely *imperative that no effort is made*. The change we want can only be achieved by this thinking process. Any effort will be an interference and cause problems.

The overall quality that we need in order to function well is one of looseness and expansiveness – and we can bring this about by bringing our attention to ourselves and our situation, and by thinking. This is possible because this quality is natural and inherent to the efficient working of our body and how our species has evolved over millions of years. Our body 'knows' how to be this way if we let it. It was Alexander who discovered that this quality exists naturally in the healthy vertebrate, but is lost in humans by the onset of habits. In order to achieve this quality of free expansiveness in a simple way, F.M. Alexander broke it down into a series of separate steps that we can think of individually. Eventually we learn to perform one step while adding the next step and then the next, and so they combine together to bring about the overall quality that we desire. We will now go through these steps in a little detail and I will summarise them afterwards so you can clearly see how they link together.

Learning to free your neck

Of all the parts of our body, our neck is one of the most important from a postural point of view, because it supports our heavy head. The relationship of our head, neck and back is all-important. If our head is held in an off-balance position it will affect everything else. We need to allow our head to balance freely on the top of our spine at a point between our ears; this point is much higher than most people realise.

To free our neck we must first bring our attention to it and our head balance. We must ensure that our head is not pulled backwards by muscle tension in the back of our neck. For most of us, it will be helpful for us to allow our nose to drop a few millimetres so that our head rolls forwards on the top of the spine. Don't drop your neck forwards like a giraffe, nor tuck your chin in. Remain upright. We're allowing our head to roll forwards slightly on the very top of our spine at a point between our ears. Gravity will do the job for us. Think of your head teetering, freely. You need to *wish* it free. It should be a clear wish that has meaning and which can bring about a change. We need our neck to be free all the time. There is normally no reason for us to tighten our neck muscles. We should not hold our head in a fixed position that we think is correct. Let it balance freely like a young child's.

We can free up throughout our whole body in a similar way, by 'telling' and intending ourselves to become freer. Habitual tension will remain unless we intervene. Tell your shoulders to be free and loose, and also your arms and legs.

Becoming expansive

As we have evolved to be expansive it is necessary that we release unwanted tensions as these have a compacting and shortening effect on us. Alexander's method helps us achieve this. We're thinking on a conscious level to tap into the instinct we have from birth for healthy upright poise. And remember that we've all got this instinct and we've also got the intricate balancing and postural mechanisms to help us; so we have the systems in place, and the ability. We only need to send the instructions to overcome our habits. We're going to create the quality of expansiveness first by bringing our attention to ourselves and then by clearly wishing and intending.

We are now going to break down this overall quality of expansiveness into easy-to-apply stages: loosening, then lengthening, then widening. But before any of this, we must stop to give ourselves time to think.

Loosening

In order to lengthen and widen we first need to release tensions that are fixing us in the posture we have at the moment. So we must inhibit doing anything to give ourselves time to free up throughout our body. We can do this either sitting or standing, and it's achieved by thinking. We are not required to shake ourselves or do anything physical except just release the tension. It must be your wish to let it go. If we carry on loosening and did nothing else we would start to collapse, so we also have further thoughts or Directions that lead to expansion.

Lengthening

Start by freeing your neck of unnecessary tension in the way described above. This is similar to releasing the handbrake in your car so you can go somewhere. Allow your whole body weight to go down through your heels into the floor. You need to be grounded as you lengthen.

While continuing to keep it free of tension, now think of your whole head going upwards. Do not push. It is essential that you inhibit the tendency to make any physical effort at all, but simply tell or wish it to happen and allow your head to go that way. You must intend your head to go upwards.

To be more precise, the direction in which you should think of your head going is not exactly vertical, but a few degrees forwards of the vertical. Free your neck first then send your head in this forward and upward direction.

Now add to this the idea of your back lengthening. Again I emphasise that you must not make any physical attempt to push yourself upwards or to adjust yourself in any way. Inhibit. You release your head upwards. We are relying on your body's natural instinct to adjust itself in response to receiving these messages from your brain. Do not worry about how it works. Your body knows instinctively because it's the natural way we are all supposed to be. It will work if you think in the right way. Think your whole back to lengthen, from your sacrum right up to your head.

A word of explanation: by thinking these thoughts we are not going to continue growing to become 10 feet tall. However, this 'need' to lengthen is as natural as the cat or dog that sends its head forwards when it walks or runs, as this activates the back and leg muscles. We need to do the same. Our own back and leg muscles are activated by this need for our head to go upwards.

Widening

We also need to widen in stature. This is achieved in a similar way, by thinking. First we must stop and inhibit, and give ourselves time to think, then, while keeping our neck free and thinking upwards, we direct ourselves to widen across our back, shoulders and whole body. Again, it is our wish that brings this about. This process does not necessarily make us physically wider unless we were narrowing in the first place. But widening in stature is an important part of helping our back muscles to co-ordinate in a strong and supportive manner.

Directing your knees

We should also think of our knees going away from our hips so as to lengthen our thighs. The precise Direction if we were bending is 'forwards and away' from each other. This helps to avoid unwanted tensions bringing them together in a knock-kneed manner. The combined Direction of 'knees forwards and away' helps to release unnecessary tensions in the legs and lower back and makes us dynamic.

When our neck is free of tension, and when our head is going upwards and when our back is lengthening and widening, and our knees are going forwards and away all at the same time, our co-ordination will improve; this maintains support throughout our body to keep us upright and to move freely without any sense of effort. This quality is likely to be different from what we normally experience, so it can only be achieved if we give ourselves time to think.

If we move without thinking, our habitual manner of movement will kick in, so we must stop to think. We must first inhibit our response to a stimulus to give ourselves time to choose how we are going to do it. We are going to choose to do the activity with a free neck and our head going upwards and our back lengthening and widening.

I mentioned earlier that in order to achieve this total quality of expansiveness, Alexander broke it down into a series of steps in a particular order. Following these steps ultimately achieves the combined quality we all had as young children of an overall free expansiveness. It requires you to pay attention to how you are, and how you are doing things. This is the sequence.

The Sequence of Steps

1. First **stop** to allow yourself to think. This is called Inhibition. This gives you time to tell your body how you would like it to be, i.e. stop to give yourself time to think step 2.

2. Think of being free all over. We don't need half the tensions most of us carry around. Tell yourself to become looser. Really wish it. Allow your weight to go down through your heels so you are grounded.

3. **Free your neck.** Let your head roll forwards a little on the top of your spine at the height between your ears by dropping your nose a few millimetres. Avoid tucking your chin in. Allow your head to teeter like a child's.

4. While letting your head balance freely, tell your **head to go forwards and upwards**. Direct your head to travel in an upward direction. Inhibit any tendency to push or make an effort. The thoughts are tapping into your instinct for good poise. Your body knows what to do. Your job is to wish for it and allow it to happen.

5. While you still maintain a free neck and the thought of your head going upwards, tell your **back to lengthen**, to follow your head. Again, do not make any physical effort to pull yourself up straight. Continue to inhibit any tendency to force or push. Do absolutely nothing physically and allow it to happen. All your back muscles will do their proper job if they receive the correct instruction.

6. While you keep the other thoughts going, instruct your **back to widen**. Think of broadening out across your shoulders, chest and back. Do not pull your shoulders back or do anything physical; this would interfere with the natural process.

7. Send your **knees forwards and away**. When you bend or when you are sitting, think your knees forwards and away from you so that your legs lengthen.

Let's recap. First, stop and inhibit. Give yourself time. Now free your neck, then send your head upwards, then tell your back to lengthen, and then your back to widen and your knees to go forwards and away. One thought after the other. Then do it again. Eventually these qualities will be happening all at the same time. But to start with, you must separate them and consider them individually. Repeat them as often as you can over and over again. However it is important to realise that they are not a mantra. Nothing will happen if we repeat these Directions like a parrot. They will only have an effect if we *mean* them to happen. It has to be the strongest wish you can muster, without using effort. We must think and intend these things to happen, one after the other. The words are almost irrelevant. It is your thoughts and clear intentions that count.

No matter what activity we undertake, this is the quality we need to have so that the machinery of our body works at its best. Whether we are running, dancing, sitting at a computer, speaking in public, tying shoe laces, feeding the dog, or slicing potatoes, we need to be free and expansive and in balance. We can overcome our habits as adults if we use our thinking and regain our natural poise.

Bending

The same principles apply to bending, picking things up and carrying. First, your attention needs to be on the matter in hand, and that is the process of bending. It's important that we are in balance before we bend or pick up any extra weight as not to do so would cause excessive strain on our body. Come as close as you can to what you're bending down towards, but inhibit first, to allow you time to free your neck and send your head upwards. Think of lengthening and widening in stature first, and then allow your knees and hips to bend at the same time. We need to bend forwards at our hips as well as bending our knees to a similar degree otherwise we will create unnecessary strain. We will move rather as a child goes into a deep squat by keeping their feet flat on the floor. We may not go down as far as the floor, but even bending a small amount will be easier if we flex our knees and hips at the same time and to a similar degree.

If we are going right down to the floor, we may be more stable if we space our feet out a little, with one foot slightly in advance of the other and turned slightly outwards. This is similar to a fencing lunge stance, but to a lesser degree. If need be, we can place a hand on a table, chair or fence to steady us. When we return to standing from being bent, we should think of leading with our head and to lengthen and widen in stature. All the time we need to be expansive. A typical harmful way of bending would be if we were to stiffen our hips and knees so that they don't bend, and then stoop downwards by arching our back in a curve. This creates a squashing effect inside us, compresses our spine and discs, and could lead to a trapped nerve and damage to the efficient working of our spine. It puts us off balance and causes excessive strain throughout our body.

When picking things up, we should be as close to the object as possible and if it's heavy hold it close to our body. Again, free our neck, send our head upwards so we lengthen as we return to standing.

Carrying

Carrying any weight can potentially put us off balance and cause strain or a twist in our body. If possible we should spread the weight across us. So bags that have a strap that crosses the body or a backpack will help spread the load, and if it's a shoulder bag, we should switch shoulders often to avoid continuous strain on one side for too long. But a good tip is to carry as little as possible and only what we need. If carrying a box, we should bring it close to our body and avoid leaning back from the waist. By allowing our ankles to be free, we can compensate for the weight in front by coming back from our ankles so that the alignment of our body remains unbroken.

Exercise: Balancing with a weight

This is an experiment to see how you can compensate correctly when carrying a weight.

You will need a heavy bag or pile of books for this exercise. Place them on a table immediately in front of you so that you can reach them easily without straining. Position yourself close to the table. Free your neck and think upwards (as previously described). You need to be upright so that you could draw a line from your ear, through your shoulder and your hips down to your ankles. So think loose and tall. Check yourself by standing side-on to a mirror.

Now pick up the heavy bag or pile of books that are just in front of you and hold them against your chest. You are going to do this exercise with an added weight to make the demonstration and experience more noticeable. Remain upright. Keep your neck free while you extend your arms forwards so that you're holding the bag or books away from you at chest height. While doing so, attempt to allow your body to come back from your ankles so that you are slightly leaning backwards to compensate for the added weight in front. Ensure that you do not arch your back nor bend in the middle in any way. Arching in your waist weakens your back and causes strain.

Bring the books back to your chest, and allow yourself to return to vertical. Note that the weight you are holding against your chest still causes you to lean back slightly. Now extend your arms carrying the weight forwards again. Remember to keep your neck free.

Allowing your body to compensate in this way is healthy. Pregnant women should also endeavour to compensate for their growing weight by coming back from the ankles. We look at this again in chapter 14.

This exercise demonstrates how a weight held in front of us changes our balance. In order to minimise strain, always carry a weight as close to your body as possible.

This chapter has summarised some of the main principles and step-by-step basic procedures of the Alexander Technique, the method that will help bring about the natural quality that we all need to function well. If we are able to follow them, we are likely to achieve a significant improvement to our health and wellbeing. When performing these guidelines, we may not notice very much happening at first, but if continually applied, this new awareness and use of our body and mind will bring about deep and important changes. We need to have a quality of free expansiveness and balance, no matter what we are doing. The more we apply ourselves to it, the more benefit we will gain. The changes aren't just switched on like a light switch. They happen progressively, and over a period of time we are likely to notice a considerable difference to our whole lives. This technique is something that we can learn to use for ourselves and can not only improve our lives now, but also help ensure that we avoid problems occurring in the future.

People having lessons in the Alexander Technique often leave the lesson feeling rather different as a result of the changes to their co-ordination. They may also feel looser, taller, lighter, calmer and more clear-headed. Gradually the changes become more permanent. You can help yourself enormously if you can apply some of the Directions described in this chapter. Give yourself some time to experiment with them right now.

IN A NUTSHELL

- **The Alexander Technique is a method we can use to help ourselves.**
- **It works by thinking – not by making an effort.**
- **By following the step-by-step procedure you can revive your natural instinct for being free and expansive with good balance.**

HELPFUL TIPS

1. Free your neck from tension as often as you can remember. Letting your head balance freely on the top of your spine will influence your whole body.
2. Take time to go through the step-by-step procedure.
3. When carrying heavy weights keep them close to your body, and avoid leaning backwards from your waist: come back from your ankles.

It's the Way That You Do It

Most of us perform dozens of different activities throughout each day, some of which we may consider good for us and others positively bad. Occupations such as sitting at a desk and typing may be thought of as bad for us while other activities such as jogging are good for us! However, if we look at two people doing the same activity, for instance typing a letter, we may notice that they are sitting in different ways: one may be twisted or hunched and tapping the keyboard with a lot of vigour, while the other may be upright and relaxed. It can also be the case that one will complain of backache and tired wrists while the other does not. The same activity can be done in quite different ways.

If we suffer some pain such as backache from sawing a piece of wood, or stiff wrists when typing we can easily pass it off with, 'Oh well, that's life.' It rarely occurs to us that our problems may lie in the manner in which we're performing the activity rather than the activity itself. In other words, it's not what you do but the way that you do it!

Mike is a sales director and regularly makes formal presentations within and outside his company. Although he is good with people on a one-to-one level, he was not comfortable in himself when speaking to large groups. He experienced a tight throat when presenting and his voice quickly became weak and hoarse.

Mike was not aware of what he was doing when he spoke. He had a distinct tendency to brace his legs, hunch his shoulders, and lean downwards on the table in front of him and also drop his neck forwards and down. While talking he was shortening his stature, depressing his larynx and tightening his neck. Consequently he suffered stress and unless he did something about these tendencies, he would probably find presenting in public increasingly difficult.

During sessions with me he became freer and able to retain his full height and stature while talking. He ceased to lean on the table or lectern when making a presentation and this helped him avoid his problem of hoarseness. His breathing has improved and the tightness in his throat hasn't recurred.

Small postural habits that we may have when young can become more and more pronounced so that as we grow older they can become a serious problem unless checked. It's therefore worth doing something about them.

We all want to be able to do things well, but let's look at a different definition of what 'doing well' could mean. It's normally considered that doing well means we've coped with a difficult day, produced the required result, a product expertly made, on time and within the allotted budget. Great! If we've performed the piano recital beautifully, we've done well. If we get the report finished on time, we've done well. If we make our business presentation and the management bought the idea, then we've also done well. But supposing we look at *how* we've done the tasks, can we give ourselves the same pat on the back? Let's take a different view. If we didn't tense our muscles unnecessarily, were in good balance, not interfering with our breathing, and if we were free, tall and expansive in stature, and used a minimum of effort, then we could say we had done the job really well. If we had achieved this, is it possible that we would have coped better, not exhausted ourselves, and been less stressed?

Hiromi is managing director of the holding company for the European division of a large Japanese advertising agency. He enjoyed running, but found he could not run for more than five minutes without experiencing severe pain in his upper back and extreme fatigue in his legs. Hiromi had previously received treatment from chiropractors and other specialists in various fields, but although he found some relief from his problems, the symptoms just returned again a few days after each session. I worked with him to reduce his habitual tension, refine his balance and help him come up to his proper full height and stature. While having Alexander Technique lessons from me, Hiromi continued to have occasional chiropractic sessions to supplement our retraining of his co-ordination.

As a result of learning to loosen, lengthen and widen, he found that he could run better by actually making less effort. His tendency to sway dramatically from side to side when walking was also reduced as he became straighter and more upright. Hiromi says that he no longer has back problems, and can now run for twenty minutes without any back pain or tiredness in his legs. It wasn't the running that was causing him grief, but the manner in which he was doing the running.

Tiredness affects our performance

Tiredness is our enemy when we want to perform well, because we inevitably start to collapse and sink downwards in stature. We lose our poise with fatigue, and in our attempts to keep going and to do well, we're more than likely to make more effort and stiffen. There will be occasions when we may say that we're just too busy to stop for rest, and things need doing urgently, and we've got too many tasks to do to allow us the luxury of sleep. Well, I'd suggest that sufficient rest is not a luxury, but an essential component to ensure that we can function effectively, and we must give ourselves the time. It is either that or we suffer the consequences. We may be able to cope with a lack of sleep for a day or two, but we will surely suffer, and our effectiveness and productivity will decline if we continue under these conditions.

Tools for the job

For any piece of machinery to work efficiently in the way it was designed, it needs to be maintained and used well. If we misuse a piece of equipment it will cease to work effectively. For instance, if I wanted to put a screw into a wall, I should use a screwdriver. But if I can't find one and use the end of a knife, or a small chisel instead, I might get the screw in, but at what cost? I would spoil the cutting edges and they would not be much good any more for their original purpose. Similarly, if I misuse my physique and get off balance, develop unnecessary tensions to compensate and repeat this pattern consistently I will be spoiling my co-ordination so that it won't function well when I need it most. Although I got the job done, one may question whether it was appropriate to expend so much energy, and damage the working parts to such a degree in the process. We're all very cost-conscious these days, but do we consider the real cost to ourselves?

Gillian worked as a secretary in a firm of solicitors, and when typing it didn't take long for a burning sensation to appear in her neck and shoulder muscles, and for her wrists and forearms to ache.

She wasn't aware that it was her postural habits that were interfering with her ability to work efficiently. Gillian tended to hunch over her keyboard, thrusting her head and neck forwards to peer at the computer screen, so putting her head severely off balance and causing neck tension. She also arched her wrists and tensed her forearms, punching her keys with stiff fingers and generally using far too much effort in the process.

During a course of sessions with me, Gillian learned how to sit more upright in a free manner without dropping her head forwards. She also practised not stiffening her wrists while typing. She heightened her office chair so that her elbows were higher than her wrists when typing and rested her feet on a foot-stool to help avoid tensing her hips. We worked on her whole co-ordination and she eventually found that she could perform her secretarial duties with much less strain and her symptoms disappeared.

Most of us will consider what end result we want to achieve, and then go all out to attain it. We focus on getting the job done, and getting it done quickly because there are another ten jobs waiting. We're in a hurry, but this trait can become a pattern, with disastrous results.

In golf, we swing the golf club with the intention of getting the ball into the hole, and in the process of wishing and praying for it to go into the hole 50 metres away we can take our eye off the ball at the critical moment. As F.M. Alexander, the originator of the Alexander Technique, clearly illustrates in his book *The Use of the Self*, if the golfer is worrying about the end result he'll never be able to keep his eye on the ball, no matter how hard he tries. He worries about where the ball is going, rather than attending to the process of playing a good stroke. He's not in the present, but thinking about the future, about the ball in the hole.

But of course the ball doesn't go into the hole until it gets there, and the process of getting it there relies on attending to the situation at the present moment, when we're swinging the club. We're trying to gain our end result on a trial and error basis without giving appropriate consideration to *how we're doing it*. Naturally, our inability to keep our eye on the ball is not the only reason we don't produce a good stroke, but just one symptom of a pattern of poor co-ordination that influences everything we do. Being on the golf course and trying to hit the ball well simply shows up our problems more clearly.

As our efforts are unsuccessful, we try harder and harder still to do better, but with each attempt we employ our habits that caused the problem in the first place. And with our increased effort, we apply our faulty co-ordination and habits even more forcibly and only succeed in making things worse. Yet everything we do feels right, because our habitual use is with us every day.

Precision and high performance

Being at the sharp end of any profession or activity throws our habits into focus. We can slide through life, performing our various activities without being aware of the effects of our habits. But when we want to win the tennis match, walk elegantly down the wedding aisle, or make a speech at our young brother's wedding, putt the golf ball into the hole from 20 metres, or even thread a needle, then our habitual tendencies really make themselves known. Suddenly, when we're put on the spot and need to perform to our absolute best, we find ourselves struggling. If we're a sportsperson, every split second counts. If we're a professional musician or singer, every subtlety and nuance make a difference. If we're an actor, or a television presenter, or chairman at the AGM, then our habitual tendencies show themselves and they will undoubtedly undermine our performance and characterise every gesture we make.

Whatever we do, it is our whole selves that we bring to the task, not just one little bit. When writing with a pen it's not just our fingers that are working. The activity involves the use

PERFECT POISE, PERFECT LIFE

of our neck, back, arms, as well as our legs and feet; the condition of our entire body will affect how we write. And if we are suffering from painful fingers and wrist, then the problem is not likely to be restricted to this location.

If we can eliminate some of our postural habits we will be more likely to achieve our desired result. We will probably do it more efficiently, effectively and with less effort. It's not what we do, but the way that we do it that is important.

Bonnie is an accounts manager for a large book publisher. Her work takes her all over the country, so consequently she spends hours behind the wheel of her car. Bonnie came to me for some sessions in the Alexander Technique to improve her posture in the hope that this would relieve her backache, stiff neck and shoulders. I worked with her to encourage her over-tense muscles to release and improve her balance.

She knew that she was sitting taller because each time she got into her car after a session, she had to adjust the rear-view mirror. I suggested to Bonnie that she also adjust her car seat so that it was more upright, and bring it forwards a little so she could reach both the pedals and the steering wheel easily without stretching. The tendency to hunch her shoulder and poke her neck forwards was reduced and she found that not only could she drive far more comfortably, but her whole sense of wellbeing was improved. And now that her posture was more naturally upright, she also had far more confidence in herself.

Exercise: Changing how we do something

Choose an activity that you feel causes you some strain. This may be just sitting at a desk, ironing or typing at a computer. To reduce the strain you should change the way you do it. So you may decide to sit down when ironing and adjust the height of the board so that your elbows and forearms are level. You may let the iron do the work rather than pressing it downwards and straining your neck and shoulders. If you are at work, you may choose to raise or lower your chair so that, again, your wrists are not higher than your elbows and your feet remain flat on the floor. Adjust the lumbar support and arm rests to suit. Remember to release your shoulders and neck too. You do this by choosing to free them. A little thought as to how we're doing an activity may be a real benefit in avoiding strain.

In the next chapter we will be looking at how we can be in effective control of ourselves, and our performance.

IN A NUTSHELL

- It's not the task or activity that's the problem: it's the way we're doing it.
- Overtiredness can make us collapse in stature, feel heavy and use more effort than necessary.
- Postural habits will undermine our best efforts so we can never achieve our best. Getting rid of them will help us do everything better.

HELPFUL TIPS

1. Consider how you are doing things rather than worrying about the end result.
2. Keep your eye on the ball. Work on the task in hand and let the end results take care of themselves.
3. Use less effort, stay free of unnecessary tension and maintain good balance while you're doing it.
4. When writing, see if you can hold your pen more lightly, and when typing at the computer do so with less tension and looser fingers.

Control to Enhance Your Life

Being in control of ourselves, and of the situations around us, is usually desirable and helpful. But it needs to be in a way that is free and not rigid. There are two types of control I wish to discuss. First, control-freakery; we can see how easy it is for control to be used in a manner that is restrictive and stifling to the point of being harmful. Second, how we can be more in control of ourselves. Rather than controlling in a way that is limiting, we can allow ourselves more freedom, release the negative habits that hold us back and live our lives to the full.

For some people, being in control can be taken to extreme levels: they are not only trying to control themselves but also their surroundings. I've even heard some people describe themselves as a 'control freak', and they can't stand the idea of not being in charge of everything around them. They want control not only of their appointment schedule, but the meetings they attend and the outcome and the decisions, their social situation, what the children are doing, and whether the dog goes out for a pee before dinner or directly afterwards. The uncertainty of not knowing how something is going to turn out drives them nuts. I would see this situation not as a problem in itself or just an idiosyncrasy, but symptomatic of an overall condition.

We could ask, is it really necessary to be in charge to such a degree, or could it be a little less pressured to allow some things to take their own natural course? Our fears may originate from childhood or another early life experience that has developed into a lifelong tendency. We may have been hurt, or our confidence shattered by some awful event, or we may have picked up the trait from our parents. We may feel inadequate in some ways so we compensate in others. However, our emotions are inextricably linked to our physical tendencies and general sense of wellbeing.

Free poise, free mind

We've already looked at the importance of not getting out of balance because this sets up a reaction to the threat of falling over. We will tense up and not breathe well, which will add to our sense of anxiety and can become habitual. Such conditions serve to make us a nervous individual, whether we are aware of it or not, and will also affect how we cope with the daily problems that life throws our way. We are already undermined, and it's likely that we'll overreact or compensate inappropriately. Needing to be in control to the ultimate degree is one method of compensation.

If we take action to correct our harmful tendencies by improving our balance, co-ordination, poise and movement, we may find that some wonderful things start to happen. As we discover better physical balance, we may find that we also become more emotionally centred and secure. And as we become more emotionally centred, many problems can start to seem like water off a duck's back: they're no problem at all. Indeed we may wonder what all the fuss was about before!

So by improving our co-ordination and use of ourselves we may find that there is less need to be so controlling in our lives. And not only that, it may be a lot more exciting to be less controlling of everything around us, so that the unexpected can have an opportunity of coming our way. What a fantastic change that might be for us! Our whole life could take a different direction and we find that we're doing all sorts of new things that we wouldn't have expected before.

Going with the flow

The idea of 'going with the flow' may not be a comfortable one if our tendency is to control everything. Sometimes we can interfere to an extent that prevents some wonderful things from happening. We may have a preconceived idea of the outcome, but it's quite possible that something unexpected could come our way if we were open to it. Sometimes I've found myself thinking of an activity that I would like to do, and decide to make the necessary phone calls and arrangements. But for some reason things don't go smoothly and my attempts to get it sorted out are thwarted at every turn. At this point I reconsider if this is really 'for me right now' and maybe I should wait, or try again later. By taking this attitude, I've invariably found that things happen that I couldn't possibly have anticipated: the tickets became cheaper the next day, a friend turned up unexpectedly, I avoided road congestion after an incident, someone phoned who could make a difference, and it's all turned out for the best. None of us knows what's going to happen next or how events or other people's actions that we aren't aware of may affect us. An attitude of going with the flow can offer many rewards. We only need to be open to the possibility of the unexpected and to welcome it, as even problems can bring you unexpected bonuses.

Our habits are in control

Let's take a look at our friend who really likes to be in control of her life, and who openly admits to being a 'bit of a control freak'. Here she is, making sure that everything is going according to her plan, and nothing is happening without her knowledge; she may be sitting in a rather held posture, stiffening her neck and tightening her shoulders and not breathing freely. If you asked her how her neck and back are, she might well complain of a bit of backache and a stiff neck. So who is in control? Is she standing and holding herself in the way she would like? Not at all. It's her habits that are in control of her; in fact she is their victim and however much she would like to think that she is the one in control, unfortunately she is not. She is deluded. And just as much as our sensory perception is corrupted by the effects of habitual tensions, so too are our sensibilities. However the situation is not entirely lost.

Helping yourself

It is often the case when things aren't going so well, or we're physically out of sorts, that we look for the solution outside ourselves. If we've got a problem with our body, then we choose the doctor to sort us out, or the surgeon, or we take a pill. And of course there are times when this is the best approach. But there are a whole lot of situations regarding our health and well-being where we can help ourselves, probably better than anyone else. This is because we are the ones in control of our body and by using our self-awareness we can help ourselves enormously. Don't get me wrong. I'm not suggesting that next time you have toothache you go to the garage and get the drill out, put your head in a vice and do a bit of DIY. We need expert assistance for a myriad of things, and it keeps everyone in business and helps to make the world go round. But there are occasions when we should look inwards rather than outwards for help.

Mind and body communication

Most people don't realise that they can be more self-sufficient, and the one big advantage we've got to help us is the size of our brain. Heavy as it is, and needing a big skull to hold it, our brain comes in pretty handy. We know some of what our grey matter is capable of and scientists are constantly learning more. But we use our brain all the time and take so much of it for granted. If you decide that you'd like to make a cup of coffee, your hands will magically reach out and grab the coffee, fill the pot with water, and set it on to the stove. If you want to go shopping, your legs will carry you all round town.

We can use our brain in a similar way to change how we are inside. Most people aren't aware that they can influence the muscular condition within their body for themselves. Let's have a little experiment, right now.

Take this book in your left hand, and tighten your right hand to make a fist as though you were going to punch someone. Go ahead and do it now. Okay, now unclench your hand so that your fingers and thumb are relaxed. Now why did you do that? You may say that I asked you to, but it was your brain that decided to go along with the little experiment and tighten your hand in the manner I described. And because you mentally agreed, the thought sent messages through your nervous system for your muscles to tighten, and 'hey presto' they did. You also chose to relax your hand afterwards from a condition of tension.

Choosing to change

In the same way we can learn to become more in control of our muscles and overcome our habitual tendencies. If you choose to loosen your hand, it will become loose. If you choose to free your neck, it will also become freer. If you decide that you're not going to hunch your shoulders any more, they will begin to release. It may take a few moments or indeed minutes or even days of repeated thinking in the right way, but eventually the habitual tensions will be reduced.

Time to think

In order to make these sorts of choices, however, we need to allow ourselves time to think. This may require only a split second, but if we don't think before we act, our habits will rule the situation and govern the quality of the outcome rather than our conscious choice and we will only succeed in making our habits even more engrained. By giving ourselves time to think, we have the choice of how we act.

Our tendency to rush can put us immediately off balance, and at the same time we're probably thinking of something other than what we're doing at the present moment, denying ourselves time to think about what we're actually doing and how we're doing it.

The potential for considerable change is within our control. It's just that most of us haven't yet learned to apply ourselves to it.

Having decided to take control, we need to know what we should do. It's quite likely that a problem we feel we have is not actually the problem itself but only a symptom. In other words, the feeling that we have a weak back, stiff neck, or that our voice isn't as strong as we'd like, or we get headaches, or we feel shy and insecure, are all no doubt symptoms of a bigger issue. It's also quite unlikely that we will be able to identify the precise source of these problems because we have been living with our conditions for such a long time. They feel normal. When it comes to our habits, they feel right. They fit with our sensory perception of what we feel is 'us'. We have the potential for self-help, but the key of course is to know exactly what to do or think. The guidelines in chapter 6 are there to help you with this.

Conscious control

Conscious control is a main theme of F.M. Alexander's and the cornerstone of his technique. It is thanks to his discoveries that we are now aware of the degree to which we can help ourselves and how we can go about it.

We all have the ability within ourselves to be more in control than we are. We have seen how habits can become engrained so that they influence virtually everything we do. It is possible for us to extend our ability to control what our body is doing, and *how* our body is doing things.

Our body and mind are beautifully integrated and it's hard, if not impossible, to separate what is mental and what is physical when it comes to movement and bodily functioning. Think of all of those millions of electronic signals that are constantly communicating between brain and body. Is picking up a pencil simply a function of our muscles? Of course the idea and command originate in our brain. And just as we can choose to perform an activity like send a text message from our mobile phone, we can choose how we do it. In other words, we can lift the phone higher to see what we're doing rather than stooping downwards, stiffening our neck and shoulders. We can choose to free our necks when we look at the screen, and avoid holding our breath.

We can use our ability to control how our body is functioning in a positive way to ensure that the wrong thing doesn't happen. The right thing will take care of itself. Our body will function beautifully if we let it; in other words, if we can avoid the habitual interferences that disturb it.

We can avoid causing unnecessary wear and tear and ensure that things don't go wrong in the future. After all, prevention is better than cure. It is never too late to start. And when people tell me that it's not possible to 'teach an old dog new tricks', I just remind them that they are not an old dog. Nor are we doing tricks. We are reviving an instinct that we've had from birth for good poise and a healthy use of our bodies. As humans we all have the ability to *choose* in ways that other animals cannot, and we can do it right into old age. And if we have more awareness of ourselves we can help ensure that we are functioning well. Even when we're over a hundred years old we can make significant changes to ourselves, as I will show you later.

Control need not be seen as harmful, limiting or restrictive, but as positive; of ensuring that we allow ourselves to function well. In order to be in control, we need to develop our awareness so that we are more conscious of what and how we are doing things. I am often asked when the new way will become automatic and when they can stop thinking about it. My answer is that every single time we think as we act and change the way we're doing things, we are breaking down and weakening the habits. Gradually the new ways become engrained, just as our bad postural habits did. We can change this cycle right now. However, even when we've made good progress and changed significantly, it's dangerous to rely on our subconscious to maintain this for us, as our habits are well established, and we want to ensure that they don't creep back in when we're not looking!

Exercise: Texting

Pick up your mobile and, as you do, free your neck by allowing your nose to drop a millimetre or so; think your neck free. Allow your shoulders to be relaxed and wide. Raise your phone higher so that you can see what you're doing rather than dropping your head and shoulders in a stoop. Be aware of how you are holding it. Are you gripping or tightening unnecessarily? Relax your grip; the phone won't jump away! Press your keys gently while keeping your neck free of tension. Avoid frowning and straining to see. Bring it up closer to you if need be. Be aware of being upright and loose – and enjoy it.

IN A NUTSHELL

- By improving our balance and poise, we may feel more centred emotionally with less need to be quite so in control of things around us.
- Better poise makes us more naturally confident and self-assured.
- Conscious control can be seen as a positive means of ensuring that the wrong things do not happen. The right thing will take care of itself.
- We can gain more control of ourselves if we use our thinking to remove the habits that govern every action we make.

HELPFUL TIPS

1. Experiment with allowing yourself to go with the flow. You may be surprised at what comes into your life.
2. Keep yourself loose and in balance. This is a different form of control that will help you cope with life's circumstances better.
3. Think of how you are doing things. Decide to keep your neck free as you do everyday activities such as phoning, texting, writing or ironing.

The Right Attitude

I meet so many people through my work who do not feel that there is anything they can do to help themselves, and it is up to the specialist to sort them out. It is also a common mistake to believe that the head and the body are separate entities whereas in reality they are inextricably linked. The fact that we have psychologists and physiotherapists who specialise in their own fields does nothing to help change this view, although it must be said that a specialist approach is often needed to provide the expertise required.

But we don't need a degree in anatomy and physiology to realise that it is our brain that controls our body. Whatever we decide to do, whether making a cup of coffee or driving the car, it is our brain that sends messages throughout our body to instruct our muscles to perform the desired activity. The same approach, as we discussed earlier, can be used to encourage tense muscles to release, and for a stooped posture to come upright. Realising that we are all capable of making a difference is the first major step in changing our lives. However, there is an essential ingredient required in order for this to work.

I understand fully when people tell me that they're not prepared to believe in something until they get some proof that it actually works. Fine, some things are difficult to comprehend until we've had the experience of it happening. This is one good reason why one needs to have a few one-to-one sessions for instance in the Alexander Technique where the practitioner can show us the difference it can make. But to enable us also to get the experience of helping ourselves, we really have to enter into the technique with an open mind and maybe a dash of enthusiasm. We need to give it a go. With clear guidance and instruction from a specialist who is able to assess our needs, we'll be able to learn a whole new way of moving and looking after ourselves. We can then rest assured that we are applying the principles, as described in chapter 6, in the most appropriate manner for our particular situation. If we follow the guidelines, then we'll not go far wrong.

Belief in ourselves

If we're able to find even a faint glimmer of a thought that we may be able to do something for ourselves, then we are tapping into some of the potential we've inherited from our ancient ancestry. We are all highly integrated human beings with the capability for a great deal of control over ourselves and our environment. It is this belief, albeit small at first, that can have a dramatic effect on how we are. The belief is the trigger. Once we start to believe that we can make a difference within ourselves, even just by thinking, we're opening up all sorts of possibilities. This principle can be applied to so many other things in life, and when people say 'I can't do that,' they are setting up a thought pattern that may well prevent them from doing so. Instead, let's say to ourselves something like, 'Hey, I may not have done this before, but there's no proof that I can't do it, and I won't know until I've tried, so let's go for it.' Then we are giving ourselves the best opportunity for success. We may go on to achieve some wonderful things in life.

Beyond our comfort zone

This approach to helping ourselves can be extended into other aspects of our life. When we start to free up physically, it will have positive effects on us emotionally too. We can become more confident and go beyond our comfort zone. Have you ever thought that you might do something that you haven't done before, something that is a little demanding or about which you feel uncomfortable or possibly downright scared? It doesn't need to be an activity like jumping out of an aircraft at 12,000 feet and doing freefall. On the other hand it could be! Or maybe give a talk to a hundred people, or jump across a small ravine gap but with a 50-foot drop, or run a marathon, or tell someone that you love them, or go on stage at the comedy club and tell your favourite joke, or make it up with your friend after a disagreement and say it's your fault just to save the friendship. Can you think of something that you may have been faced with in the past, or wanted to do, but a voice inside says, 'No, you can't!' or 'No, this isn't for you!'? Have you heard that voice that stops you from doing it? It's the voice that overrules your heart, limits you and holds you back. Where does that voice come from and why does it appear?

Don't let the past undermine you

During our lives we are constantly living new experiences, some of which are good and some are bad. All experiences have a profound effect not only on our consciousness but also on our subconscious. Having a good experience tells us that it's okay and that we're good at this and we can do it again. It's positive and we feel that there is no need for fear. Having a bad experience, particularly when we're young, tells us that this is hurtful and painful, and that we're not successful, that we're a failure, and it makes us timid when a similar situation occurs. So we go through our lives, constantly experiencing things that add to and change our perception of ourselves and our abilities or limitations.

If I go on stage and make a presentation as I have done hundreds of times and it goes well, without suffering nerves, then this positive experience tells my subconscious that it's okay, I can do this and it's likely to go well when I do it again. Conversely, if it doesn't go well then this negative experience can affect me on subsequent occasions. This happened to me once many years ago.

I was in Amsterdam on business with some colleagues as a young up-and-coming manager and we had an important meeting with the directors of a large Dutch retail organisation. I had been out late the night before, and having had some drinks, not slept well, then had a salty breakfast and become rather dehydrated, I was very much the worse for wear. I went into their boardroom with my colleagues from London at 9.00 a.m. on the top floor of their corporate offices where the windows went from floor to ceiling and the hot sun was blasting in. When it was my turn to speak, I completely dried up, couldn't think properly and felt a strong sense of panic. I went pale and only managed to splutter something and make my excuses for not feeling well.

This type of experience can seriously undermine our confidence, as it goes into our subconscious and tells us that this situation is fearful. Next time we're confronted by a similar one, we will feel nervous, if not downright frightened. Our inner voice tells us that we should fear the situation as a source of discomfort and distress. We won't feel good, but threatened.

This bad experience affected me deeply. During the short period leading up to my next presentation, I was checking for signs of my fear. I was almost trying to find my fear, just to confirm that I really was frightened! And with every attempt to find the fear in me to justify my nervousness, I was reliving the bad experience, and further engraining the negative habit that was undermining me. And I found it. Indeed I managed to create it by looking for it. By finding the nervousness I was satisfying my ego in some perverse way. I had actually made myself fearful, even though it was all in my imagination: the feeling was one that I had created for myself, and had never experienced before.

Not only did I have the voice inside shouting that I should run away and be fearful, I also had my muscles wanting to tighten up to stiffen my neck, shoulders, legs and back in a fight or flight response that would also throw me off balance and make me hold my breath. However, by using the Alexander Technique I was able to inhibit these tendencies and eventually overcome this problem. While in Amsterdam, I was undermined by excessive tiredness and dehydration, making it particularly difficult for me to consciously take control to ensure that I didn't respond in that manner.

This happened over twenty years ago and is now a distant memory. I regularly give public presentations these days and thoroughly enjoy them.

Our physical condition is strongly linked to our emotions, and one affects the other. If I am able to control myself so that I don't stiffen, and maintain good balance and breathe easily, I'm not setting up the physical response to fear and I'll be more likely to remain calm and be successful. The recurring thought that I can't do that and the physical tendency to stiffen are both habits: one mental and the other physical, that is if they are capable of being separated at all.

From these sorts of bad experiences we get an attitude about our abilities. For instance, being scolded constantly by our parents for not doing well enough at school can have quite an effect on our self-perception. We may eventually feel that we are not and cannot be successful. We may grow to lack self-confidence, and also have a poor sense of our worth. So when we are confronted with challenges outside our comfort zone, we may subconsciously believe that there is no point in trying to achieve them, because deep down we feel that we don't have the ability. With endless verbal attacks and a lack of emotional support from our parents, we may also have developed certain postural characteristics that are based on fear and lack of self-worth, such as a hollow chest, stoop, rounded shoulders and general collapse.

Contriving posture

Some people not only develop postural tendencies without their awareness, but actively cultivate an outward appearance or manner that they feel helps give them an identity. We can see this in many young people today. Some develop the cultured stoop or slouch that James Dean could be asked to answer for, along with other mannerisms that are considered trendy or hip. A current popular attitude with many young people is to feign a lack of interest in everything. But are they really as uninterested as they would have us believe, or just play-acting? If we look closer, we may see that they are also suffering from a loss of balance and natural poise. In some cases they have purposely disengaged their supportive muscles to create their chosen slouch and 'don't care' identity. Many are hiding behind a mask of a contrived persona that has no relation to the real person underneath, possibly simply to compensate for a lack of self-worth. However, if they were truly co-ordinated, balanced and centred, they would feel so much more confident in themselves. They would feel more secure in their true personality and abilities, and have no need for such contrivance.

I'm always interested to see how people can change emotionally during sessions in the Alexander Technique. One particular young woman who came to me for sessions to help with her posture changed in more ways than she bargained for. Although very likeable, she described herself as highly stressed and driven. She held herself in quite a bad stoop and, being slight in figure, this made her even more diminutive. Her droopy posture was so bad that apparently people often asked her if someone had died! As we progressed with our lessons, not only did her posture improve, but also her demeanour. She seemed to be more relaxed

*within herself, and even got herself a new boyfriend. When I
open the door to her now, instead of the dour frown and grunted
'Good morning' I'm greeted by a friendly smile. How nice!*

I have often heard people say that their husband or wife is
so much easier to live with now that they've had some sessions
in the Alexander Technique! By changing their posture they
have become more relaxed within themselves and some of the
jagged corners of their nature seem to have been rounded off.
The defences that people can throw up, possibly in response
to fear, can make them seem unfeeling and brittle. These can
be directly linked to their physical condition and may be just
an outward manifestation of imbalance and strain throughout
their whole body.

Develop a positive attitude

In reality, we don't know that we are not capable of doing
something until we've given it a go. The automatic response
of 'I can't do that' doesn't serve us at all. In fact we are pre-
programming failure, because we're telling ourselves that we're
going to fail. And since we like to be right most of the time,
our subconscious will make sure that we do fail, just so that
we can be proved right. 'You see? You can't do it. I told you
so!' And what pleasure do we get in being right and stopping
ourselves from succeeding just to prove it? Fear of failure is
one of the biggest reasons why people do not attempt new
things in their lives.

How many opportunities and possible new futures have we

walked away from? It could be meeting a stunningly attractive person, or in business, or just having fun, or something that we may see as being risky to our ego, and we don't do it just to ensure that we aren't a failure.

On the other hand, I could say to myself, 'I know I haven't done this before, but there is no evidence that I won't be able to do it, so let's have a go.' If I tell myself that I'm going to do this, without any thought of failure, I'm more than likely to succeed. By saying to myself that I *can* do this, I'm pre-programming success. We don't know that we are unable to do something until it is actually proven, and if we don't try we'll never find out. And even if we do not succeed the first time, who's to say that we won't succeed the next?

However, there are dangers in the attitude of 'trying harder' to do something. 'Trying harder' suggests that we must make more effort to succeed. It invites more tension, and this will throw our co-ordination even further out of sync and we will be further away from success. If we want to have another go, we should pay particular attention to the way we're doing it rather than focusing on the end result, as was discussed in chapter 7.

Beginner's luck

Isn't it interesting that when we have our first go at something new we can sometimes excel beyond our expectations, surprising ourselves and our fellow colleagues? We play a golf stroke for the first time and it almost goes straight into the hole, or we roll the ten-pin bowl having never done it before and we get all ten down with one throw! But when we do it again, the success of the first attempt eludes us. I believe that this situation often occurs when we don't have any preconceived idea of how we are going to perform or any previous experience to match up to. There is no stress and we are probably relaxed and free. We have only the idea in mind of putting the ball in the hole or hitting down the ten pins and therefore we just do it. As a beginner we have not established any habits related to our performance because we've never done it before, but we may be visualising what we'd like to happen. When it comes to subsequent attempts to repeat our initial success, we are likely to have expectations. We want to repeat our good fortune so we feel that we must try hard. We end-gain. But in the process of trying harder we're setting up tensions in our body that didn't exist during our initial attempt that was so successful. In other words, we're not doing what we did the first time so how can we expect to achieve the same performance?

The self-fulfilling prophecy

In my work I meet many people who have come for assistance with their posture, co-ordination, or they want to improve their sense of wellbeing or performance. During our initial chat when I discover why they've come along and taken details of their situation, they often say to me such things as, 'I have a very stiff neck', 'I am always stressed', or 'I am a rather tense person.' Without realising it, they are actually telling themselves to be this way, because subconsciously they are constantly reinforcing the quality that they would rather not have. If, on the other hand, they were able to say to themselves that although they may have experienced problems in the past, it's not going to be like that from now on, they are going to be free, calm and confident, then they're more likely to have positive change. 'I am now different', 'I used to have a stiff neck, but I'm choosing not to have one now.' These phrases have a different ring to them, don't you think?

Whatever we're thinking is likely to have an effect on the way we are, or on how we perform our activities. 'What you think is what you get.' Changing our perception or attitude is a very big part of helping ourselves to achieve our full potential. Many people may say that this is easier said than done. And I may return to them and say you can limit yourself if you want. We can always find reasons why we shouldn't do something or why we think we can't, and by thinking this way we're almost certain to succeed in preventing ourselves from achieving something that could really be remarkable.

Always reward yourself

In order to achieve our full potential it is essential that we allow ourselves the opportunity to experiment. And when we get a positive experience because we managed to do something wonderful that we wouldn't have dreamed possible, our confidence will be bolstered and we are encouraged to go for what we want again. May I suggest that you reward yourself for it? Pat yourself on the back and buy yourself a gift, a special gift that's a real treat. You deserve it. Acknowledgement is the final stage of the process, from inspiration, planning, action – and then it's reward time! This will help you feel more positive about yourself and about going for future challenges. We may even start creating new, more exciting opportunities for ourselves.

Changing our attitudes

Changing how we approach new situations can be tricky because attitudes are habits of thinking that are just as engrained into our subconscious as our physical or postural ones, if not more so.

When you hear your inner voice it's important to let it be heard. If you know that you have this inner voice and expect it, you can detach yourself from it, and hear it as an outsider. Give it an ear as it needs to be heard, but you can choose to ignore its message as you know where it's coming from, and how limiting it is. There are many organisations offering courses and workshops that can give us the opportunity of having positive experiences in situations we may previously have found demanding and difficult. You will find some useful addresses at the back of this book for organisations such as Insight Seminars and the Essence Foundation.

However, in all circumstances relating to our abilities, well-being and performance we must also attend to the practical situation of being a biped standing in balance on two feet. Because no matter how much we try to change our mental state by whatever means, if we're still holding on to our phys-ical habits we'll never realise our best. By working consciously on our balance and co-ordination and releasing habitual tensions, then we may be able to let go of long-held attitudes and fear patterns. Our whole body, as well as emotions and thoughts, are connected, so by breaking one cycle we will help change everything else.

Frances was one person who didn't believe in herself. She had low self-esteem, was shy, and her posture was diminutive in the way that she hunched her shoulders and collapsed in front. Physically, she was suffering from pain in her back and shoulders, her breathing was not efficient, and she had regular depression and headaches. In her early thirties, Frances was worried that her condition would worsen as she got older. She had followed many forms of treatment both physical and mental, but not found much long-term benefit, so she decided to try the Alexander Technique, almost as a last resort.

Frances was sceptical when she arrived. However she decided to have some sessions and agreed to enter into it with an open mind. I asked of her that she be prepared to change, and allow things to be different, and also to participate in the sessions, and not to consider herself just as a passenger.

Gradually Frances became more upright, nearer to her full height, and she also opened out across her shoulders. With the release in tension she began to notice that her breathing was becoming freer, her tension headaches were relieved and her mood lightened. As her posture and balance improved, so did her self-esteem and confidence. With her more upright poise she also gained in presence and self-assuredness.

Exercise: Going for it

Choose something that you would not normally attempt and decide that you're going to do it. Make it something that you feel is really demanding and a stretch. This may be making a difficult telephone call, asking someone out for a date, buying yourself an indulgent present, being nice to someone you've argued with, putting yourself up for election, or sacrificing your day off to do charity work. Just see how good it feels to do something different and demanding. You'll probably be floating on air afterwards. If on the off-chance that you didn't succeed in your endeavour, look at the manner in which you did it and see if you could do it differently. And when you've done it, remember to reward yourself!

So far I have looked at how we can take more control over ourselves and our actions. I have introduced you to some of the main principles of the Alexander Technique to see how they can be applied to help overcome tensional and postural habits. I have also shown how an appropriate and positive attitude can help us achieve more, and make big changes to ourselves and our lives. In Part Three I will show you how all these principles can be applied to real-life situations such as in business, sport, performance, improving our voice, being sexy and how to live to a ripe old age in the best of health. It's also possible to cope better with some of life's challenges such as pregnancy, separation and bereavement. By applying these principles during our daily life we can help ourselves be more successful, happier and healthier and enjoy our life to the full.

IN A NUTSHELL

- Freeing ourselves from postural habits will help us change our mindset.
- Unhappy or unsuccessful experiences can create an expectation within us that we will fail again.
- Saying 'I can't' sets up a pattern for failure.
- A positive attitude helps us succeed.
- Saying 'I can' will help us in many ways.
- We don't know we can't do something until we try.
- If we approach new projects or activities with an open mind, we may be surprised at how successful we can be.

HELPFUL TIPS

1. Don't prejudge your performance.
2. In many situations we have nothing to lose by just 'going for it'.
3. Next time we are confronted with a new activity, approach it saying, 'I may not have done this before, but there's no proof that I can't do it, and I won't know until I try, so let's give it a go!'
4. Changing your posture will help change your emotions.

Part Three
Ways to Change Your Life

High Calibre, High Income

There are certain times in our lives when we feel that it is important to give a good impression of ourselves. At work, this may be at meetings, making a presentation or in an interview. Some of us may feel that such situations are not relevant to us, but for almost every job imaginable, be it in clothes design, law, accountancy, business consultancy, IT, haute cuisine, marketing, finance, retail or floristry, we've had to go through the interview process, no matter how informal it has been. And when we've got the job, we usually have personal assessments and reviews – based on our performance – throughout the year. If we want promotion and to reach the highest level it's important that we display a high-calibre demeanour all the time and not just for the one critical hour of an interview.

Let's look at a hypothetical new job interview situation. When we arrive, we are trying to keep an open mind, not to judge too soon, not to appear too anxious, yet not so laid back that we seem indifferent. We've done our homework, researched the company and got an idea about the role we'll be expected to perform. We've developed some alternative ideas so, if asked, we'll be able to put them across, showing how wizardly creative we are, up to speed on current methods and thinking and can take the job and the company forwards. The position carries a hefty salary, executive car, interest-free company loan and other executive perks. We know that if we get the job, we'll be able to enhance our standard of living considerably. 'New home with an extra room or two, afford another baby and the baby-sitter, comfortable holidays in the Caribbean . . . New lifestyle, here we come!' So we're a bit keyed up, and when the time comes to walk into the room we are understandably a little nervous and wiping the sweat from our hands. We are there in front of a group of people who want to see what we're made of and all eyes are on us. We have an impression to make, and that impression will influence their decision about us. The next hour or so is critical. We want to do our best; indeed we need to do our best so we don't feel we've let ourselves down.

But have we attended to everything possible? Are there any little things lurking that may undermine the performance of our lifetime? For instance, how is the body machinery working? Have we got a clue? Maybe we're not aware at all and just running on autopilot, trusting that the legs that brought us here don't let us collapse in front of the interviewer's desk. We trust that our body supports us throughout. But these are exceptional circumstances. This is not an everyday situation where we can drift through the work, make the odd enlightened comment in a meeting then back off when we are uncertain. This moment when our interview curtain goes up and we are the focus of attention is when we need all our systems functioning 100 per cent!

First impressions

So we've walked in, and if our daily habits are with us, we're probably a little off balance, consequently stiffening our legs and lower back and neck; nor are we breathing well. We are personable, remembering to smile, but the stoop and hunched shoulders tell a story too. Holding ourselves up straight is tiring, and we've never really found that easy since we were a child, and today is no exception. The first few moments of introduction and getting seated are a crucial stage where first impressions are made. Quoting an article in *BBCi Health*: 'Before you've even spoken to the person you've got your eye on, the way you've walked and stood is more than 80% of their first impression of you!'

Taking a seat in front of the interviewers can also be slightly unnerving, and we don't know where to put our hands. We feel self-conscious and awkward. The tensing in our neck and shoulders and our poor breathing will also weaken our voice.

It doesn't matter how tall, short or broad we are, or even how elegantly we dress. But it does matter how we carry ourselves. Body language counts for a huge amount, particularly during a first meeting. If we stand rigidly with a stiff neck and narrowed across the shoulders, we are likely to look timid or even frightened, insecure and lacking confidence. Do we give the impression of being up to the job? Is this the impression that we would ideally like to make for ourselves?

I received a call one summer from a young man who was un-employed but busked on the London Underground playing rock-

style guitar, and he said he wanted to improve his voice. When I met him, it was clear that he had the tendency to tighten his neck and shoulders in such a way as to make his voice very husky. He was a little edgy, and I got the feeling that his life had not been easy.

We had good fun in our sessions and he made a lot of progress. During the sessions we included some voice work and some humming exercises (explained in chapter 13). By the end of the summer his poise had changed, his voice was clearer, he seemed more relaxed and we parted company.

Although he was out of work and busking, this chap had a degree in economics, and a diploma in wine tasting: quite a combination! I had the good fortune to bump into him a few months later and he told me proudly that he'd got himself a job as a sales adviser for one of the large wine merchants in London. It seemed that learning the Alexander Technique had helped make changes in his posture and attitude to life to such a degree that they had helped him get a new job. I still occasionally bump into him and he always greets me with a huge smile, shakes my hand and updates me with his latest news.

Commanding stature

If we stand upright, in balance and looking comfortable and relaxed within ourselves, our manner speaks volumes about our calibre and potential. Not only do we look confident, we'll be feeling so, because, as we've already discussed, physical balance and healthy poise promote emotional centredness and with it a *natural* confidence. Our posture can serve us or undermine us, and we'll discover that it's within our ability to make positive improvements for ourselves.

We need to look after the machinery that's going to do the job. Make sure that we are functioning as well as we can, then we will be able to bring our best to the situation. We need to be well poised, free and expansive, as any unnecessary tightening of muscles will only serve to undermine us by interfering with our co-ordination. We need to ensure we are not tensing in a way that compresses our chest and larynx as this can interfere with our voice and breathing; we need the oxygen to help us think clearly. Our great performance will then not be only a one-off. It will be typical of the well-co-ordinated, relaxed and efficient person we always are.

Exercise: The semi-supine position

This procedure is recommended by most Alexander Technique teachers as a means to help release excessive muscular tension and to allow your body to lengthen and widen. It will benefit your poise when you stand up again. Lie down on your back on a carpeted floor for ten minutes with your head resting on 2–3 inches of books and your knees bent so that your feet are drawn up towards you. This is called the semi-supine position. Space your feet apart about the width of your shoulders and rest your relaxed hands on your tummy. Think of sinking down into the floor so that you let go of unwanted tension in your back muscles. Let your shoulders release and 'melt' down into the floor. After a few minutes, instruct your head to go away from your shoulders and your spine to lengthen. Do not force anything and <u>make no effort</u>. Just think. Let gravity and your body weight do the job. Lie down like this daily. It will help calm and centre you and help your posture enormously.

Dealing with stress

Being put on the spot to perform a presentation or attend an important interview can be very demanding and cause stressful symptoms. We all know that preparation is the key to success in these situations so most of us will allow time for this. If we can extend this attitude to prepare ourselves physically by releasing unnecessary tensions, improve our balance and poise, then we will be giving ourselves some fundamental support. It is simply not possible to perform at our best if we are stressing our body with postural habits and interfering with our breathing.

We can defuse stressful symptoms by taking calming drugs, but clearly this is not ideal and it would be so much better if we did not get stressed in the first place. Everything we've been discussing in this book is relevant to dealing with stress. We should prepare ourselves physically. Poor posture detrimentally affects our breathing and stressful situations can make it worse. If we're not breathing efficiently, we will get an imbalance of chemicals in the body that will add to our sense of stress. Then we're in a vicious cycle. We've got to make sure that we're breathing fully and easily. I have explained this more fully in chapter 5.

The following simple exercise can be done any time, and

will be particularly helpful just before going into an important meeting.

Exercise: Breathing out

To stimulate your breathing and to calm you down, try the following:

Sit or stand upright and 'think' your neck free. Without taking a special breath, breathe out quietly through your nose as much as you can to empty your lungs. Empty them completely, but avoid collapsing your posture. Stay upright. When you have expelled as much air as you can, release the tension around your ribs to allow them to expand and just let the air come in naturally, without effort. Do not suck or sniff air in. When you do this procedure well, you may find the air comes in in two stages, i.e. your lungs will replace what you expelled, then you may get a small amount extra. When you have completed this little procedure, breathe normally for two breaths then repeat the whole process again, up to four or five times. Do not continue to breathe this way. It is simply an exercise to stimulate your breathing. If you feel dizzy or faint, stop immediately. Return to normal breathing afterwards.

Don't leave postural considerations to chance. Attend to them now so that when you want to present your best image it comes naturally. It's not possible to switch successfully from a habitual slouch full of tension to being well poised with good co-ordination in the few minutes before you enter the interview room.

IN A NUTSHELL

- In order to help ourselves perform well in the interview situation, we need to ensure that our posture isn't letting us down, and that we're in balance and breathing freely.
- Physical tension will add to your anxiety, so ensure that you are always in balance.

HELPFUL TIPS

1. Free your neck and shoulders (as described in chapter 6).
2. Avoid leaning forwards unnecessarily. Remain upright.
3. Relax your hands and forearms.
4. Always ensure that you are not holding your breath.
5. Calm and centre yourself by frequently performing the semi-supine procedure above.
6. Attend to your posture needs now so that you're always in peak condition.

Become high calibre

Most of us have the potential for greater achievement in business and to enjoy a higher income. It is likely that you have untapped abilities not yet realised and that even more personal success is just waiting to be achieved. My belief in this has come about from my own experience of working with hundreds of people who have improved their ability to cope with stress and developed a high-calibre demeanour.

This human machine that we call 'us' is so sophisticated that we can call up reserves of power and stamina to see us through the most difficult situations almost at a moment's notice. Yet it would be harmful if not dangerous to rely on such reserves full-time in order to perform well on a daily basis. To do so would undoubtedly weaken us and eventually cause sickness.

But wouldn't it be wonderful if your 'normal' state and performance ability were moved up several notches so that you could cope more comfortably and successfully no matter how difficult or stressful the situation might be? Well, you can achieve this.

You need to attend to two major influences that affect your performance: one is the mental 'attitude' and self-perception that 'tell' you what you believe is possible based on your past experiences of success and failure; a topic that we looked at in chapter 9. Suffice to say here that to change your self-perception and the way you think will have an enormous effect on everything you do. The second is how efficiently your body and mind are working as a unified whole; you require psycho-physical unity, the subtle and sophisticated co-ordination of your whole being.

Visualise yourself

Close your eyes for a moment and picture meeting someone who carries themselves with an elegant, upright poise, who moves smoothly and unhurriedly, who looks you in the eye and talks clearly with resonance and gives you a relaxed, disarming smile. They are open across their chest and they do not cross their arms or legs to protect themselves subconsciously. Their hands are relaxed and open too. In your mind's eye observe their confidence and calmness. Do they seem in charge of their situation and do they appear trustworthy? Do they look strong yet relaxed and worthy of a high pay cheque? Of course they do. Now put yourself into this picture. See your own face in front of you. If this is where you aspire to be, then this is where you can be. Because you *can* be the way you want. It's your choice.

Exercise: Visualisation

Visualisation techniques are often used by sports people to break records and achieve new levels of performance. We can use them too, to help us perform better in business or any other situation.

Give yourself time regularly to visualise yourself behaving and performing at meetings or any situation in the way that you would ideally like. You can do this anywhere: sitting at home in a comfortable chair, or in the bath, on the train, in a waiting room, or a taxi. Allow five to ten minutes.

Close your eyes and visualise yourself performing the role of your choice in the manner you would ideally like. You may choose to visualise yourself dancing the tango superbly well at a club, participating in a meeting or presenting to a large group of people where you have the audience's complete attention and you are speaking to them clearly, calmly with relaxed authority. If you are presenting, see yourself speaking unhurriedly and with 100 per cent confidence. You are standing freely with tall, broad stature. You are relaxed inside, enjoying yourself and feeling completely secure. Or you can visualise yourself on that important date, getting the job, acting on film, being beautiful and relaxed.

Using this form of visualisation technique to improve your poise will be most effective if you are also taking practical steps to improve it by following the guidelines in this book.

Natural confidence

We're not interested in 'putting on' a pretence that creates an illusion of high calibre. We're not dealing with acting here. This is about *being* the person you have always wanted to be. There are many courses that can help with presentation skills, negotiating and how to read body language and so on, but this is not what I'm talking about. I am interested in helping you find your true calm and confidence – the *real* you, so that you can be naturally at ease at all times and have the confidence to do the things in life that you really want to do. This quality can only be discovered by ridding yourself of the learned habits that are interfering with your natural, healthy condition. When you are truly balanced, well co-ordinated, free in your joints and breathing fully, the qualities I have described will be yours without any pretence. After all, we are all meant to be this way – naturally.

In order to achieve these qualities it is necessary to attend to everything described so far in this book. In other words, we must ensure that we are in good balance, released in our muscles throughout our body rather than tensing, lengthening and widening rather than stooping, and not interfering with our breathing. This is how our body functions best.

The group managing director for a major international corporation came to me some time ago. His job required him to present to large groups of people, including shareholders at the AGM. He found that by improving his natural poise and breathing he brought to the platform a strong yet relaxed demeanour that portrayed strength and gravitas and inspired confidence. By being upright, in balance, and speaking clearly and being comfortable within himself, he gave an impression of being totally in control, and it seemed that no situation was beyond his capability to resolve. Incidentally, this same client had to travel all over the world for various meetings, and he found that being freer and better co-ordinated also helped him be much fresher after a long-haul flight. He was then far more able to perform at his best.

Improvements to my own posture when I was young made a huge difference to me professionally. In fact they helped me gain promotion.

Before I became a professional practitioner of the Alexander Technique, I had a career in marketing. I had been a nervous child and not particularly successful academically and when it came to leaving school I didn't expect to achieve much. However, I did gain a diploma in window display and this helped me get my first job as a window dresser for a large department store in Glasgow.

A year later in 1972, when I was twenty, my mother and father discovered the Alexander Technique. Mum had had a bad back and Dad was simply interested, having heard about it through his professional musical circles, so they both had lessons. They suggested that my brother and I have some lessons too, to help alleviate any problems and also as an extension of our education and as a means of helping us look after ourselves. I cannot thank them enough now for their foresight.

I thoroughly enjoyed these sessions, discovering a new sense of balance and co-ordination. I became freer, more upright and broader. My Alexander teacher told me not to buy any formal jackets for a while as I'd need a larger size. And he was right. All the physical and personal changes that took place had a profound effect on me. I broadened out and found a new confidence and belief in myself. I carried myself well and my upright relaxed demeanour served me in my work. Although I had been quite creative and good at my job, I was now much more confident, ambitious, with good posture and was considered to have possible management potential. To my surprise and delight I was offered a display management job in a menswear chain in Scotland. Four years later I moved to a large fashion chain with eighty stores where I headed up a team of forty display personnel. From there I was headhunted to join a national chain of 480 menswear stores based in London where I became a senior executive with responsibilities for in-store design, layout, sales promotion and display. Over the years I had become a good presenter and was constantly required to give presentations to large groups of executives on the marketing plans for the company.

When I reached my mid thirties, I decided that I wanted

to change my career and I had the confidence to do so. I quit, returned the large company car and forfeited the perks that I had enjoyed to enrol on a three-year full-time training course to become a teacher of the Alexander Technique, the method that had helped me achieve far more than I would have ever imagined when I was young. I now teach this technique to others, and thoroughly enjoy myself.

It became clear to me during my previous marketing career that the importance of having a good speaking voice in business cannot be overstated. It is an extremely beneficial and influential tool, yet it is a skill that is often overlooked. A good voice can exude confidence and imply reliability and high calibre. Although we are going to be discussing voice at length in chapter 13, I want to give you one example here to show how we can change our voice to the benefit of ourselves, our business and even to earn us more money.

Peter is a top-ranking European fund manager and partner in one of Europe's largest fund management companies and is personally responsible for managing over one billion US dollars in funds.

He had been criticised in an appraisal for generally speaking too quickly, giving unsatisfactory face-to-face interaction, and seeming unwilling to engage in debate. He told me that he felt particularly ineffective during international conference calls where his over-rapid presentation, possibly caused by nerves, often resulted in silence rather than the expected questions and debate. This undermined his confidence still further and weakened his business persuasiveness.

It was important from the outset that we should first work on improving Peter's overall postural condition. He learned how to inhibit his tensional habits and encourage a loosening, lengthening and widening of his stature that in turn improved his breathing, so when it came to introducing some voice work into the sessions, changing his manner of speech became easy. The emphasis was entirely on making less effort rather than more and ensuring that he maintained his upright poise throughout. Release in his chest brought about a reassuring resonance and gravitas.

I encouraged Peter to speak more slowly throughout the whole session, and particularly when we talked about some aspects of his work that he found stressful. He says himself that this has helped give him confidence and integrate his new manner of speaking into his normal life.

After just a few sessions including the voice work, Peter got positive feedback from several sources on his new clarity of delivery. Within a few weeks the new manner of speaking was coming more naturally. Conference calls and face-to-face meetings were no longer as daunting and he had grown in stature and professional demeanour. Six months later he received a salary increase.

Exercise: Speaking slowly

Experiment with talking slowly when on the phone and in meetings. Put pauses between your comments. These will add weight to your message.

Speaking quietly and slowly will encourage people to listen to you more than if you raise your voice and rush your delivery. You

---

will also allow yourself the chance to form your words more fully and add resonance. By doing so you can add power and gravitas to how you come over.

I believe that it's possible for us all to perform better at virtually everything we do. It is within us to develop a calm, centred balance that conveys our truly confident nature and professional demeanour. Through good natural poise and skilled and effective use of our voice we can sway an argument, enthrall an audience and win deals. We can bring gravitas, power and reassurance to a discussion and convey personal and professional reliability. We are all born with this capacity and with appropriate training surprising results can be achieved.

We are all performers in one way or another, whether we're in a business situation, on the tennis court, golf course, or even in social situations. We want to give our best, and we'll be looking at more ways of achieving this in the next chapter.

IN A NUTSHELL

- **There are two major influences that affect our ability to perform well: our attitude and our psycho-physical condition.**
- **Inner confidence comes naturally as a result of improving our balance, co-ordination and poise.**

HELPFUL TIPS

1. Refine your balance and ensure that you're not leaning.
2. Free your neck as frequently as possible.
3. Think tall and broad.
4. Perform the Breathing out exercise in this chapter.
5. Speak more slowly.

We're all Performers

11

Giving a performance is often considered as something that other people do. We can think that it doesn't involve us because we may not play sport competitively or play an instrument, or act, dance or sing. Yet every day most of us are in situations where we want to perform to our best ability. It might be simply remaining calm when coping with our child who's being difficult, being efficient as a receptionist when dealing with awkward situations, waiting in a restaurant, being a good airline steward, negotiating a deal, returning an item to a shop, or getting married and walking beautifully down the aisle. All these situations require us to behave or perform in a particular manner if we are to gain the desired results. We are put on the spot. It will be helpful then if we're able to think clearly, remain calm and if our body is functioning well.

Musicians, actors, dancers, singers, acrobats, golfers, tennis players, athletes or comedians know that the slightest nuance shows up enormously. If we're on stage in front of an audience every movement and subtlety of gesture contribute to our performance. If we are on the sports field, then the refinement of our physical abilities is there in our final score.

When we're at the cutting edge of any activity attention is drawn to many, many small things that in the normal course of daily life can go unnoticed, but become very exposed when under the spotlight. And when we are working to refine our abilities to the highest level, then the smallest adjustment can make huge differences. No matter what activity we perform or what job we do, it is ourselves, the big ME that we bring to the task, the whole of ME. It is the ME that has had the life I've had, with all its difficulties and hardships and pleasures, the school experiences, the parental influences, the relationships, interviews and castings, the failures, poor scores, rejections and all. As a performer in life, ME is all I've got, and I bring all of myself to the arena. When I perform, I shall find it very difficult not to allow my postural tendencies to have an influence on my work. They are there all the time, unless we've dealt with them on a day-to-day basis. It just isn't possible to switch them off effectively for a special occasion, and then return to them afterwards. They need to be dealt with properly for the long term.

We are going to look at sport in more detail further on in this chapter, so first I want to share with you a few examples relating to music and stage performance.

A young flamenco guitarist came to me with problems in his back. Sitting for long periods of time in the traditional flamenco position was putting a twist in his spine, tilting his pelvis and causing strain in his neck and shoulders. Aware that several world-class flamenco guitarists all had back problems, Michael had the foresight to try to sort his problems out early on, to avoid them worsening in later years. He had regular sessions for a while as this gave him the best chance of changing, and his overall co-ordination improved to a level where he could stand and sit normally with much less strain. His sensory perception became more reliable. He was able to feel if he was doing himself harm by twisting and making unnecessary effort, an awareness that he hadn't had before.

Michael experimented with various footstools and supports for the guitar so that he could maintain better poise and we worked together on his guitar-playing position. He was by then coming to his playing with a much greater conscious awareness than before. He can now play for long periods without strain and is hoping to build on his career as a flamenco guitarist.

Performance skills

Musicians need dexterity of fingers and the subtlest of control. Dancers need refined balance, bodily control, athleticism, superb flexibility and co-ordination. Singers need good breathing, vocal control, as well as musicianship. Actors need the ability to put themselves into a character and define their whole being through movement, voice and character idiosyncrasies, not to mention the obvious stage directions. Good sports people need excellent co-ordination as well as strength and stamina.

All these requirements mean that the performer has to be able to adapt to the demands of their situation. What will severely hamper their ability to do this are the characteristics that they've developed over the years. The sports person needs to be free of habitual tensions that will interfere with the accuracy of their game, the air steward or waitress needs to maintain good balance when carrying drinks, and the actor needs to be in a 'neutral' state, free of any limitations of their own, in order to avoid bringing those unwanted qualities into the performance. The sales person needs to be bright, alert and able to cope with difficult customers, as does anyone who deals with the general public. The singer needs to be free of the tensions that can interfere with vocal resonance, clarity and breathing. The pianist not only needs to be able to play the keyboard, but also to sit at a piano in such a way that they aren't stiffening their back, neck, arms, wrists and fingers. The violinist needs relaxed wrists, arms, fingers, shoulders and neck too. And they must be able to stand or sit for the length of the performance without getting backache or any other muscular strain or tension that may interfere with their performance.

Most stage performers want to present a powerful stature that has a presence; to appear commanding to an audience and be free of nerves: all qualities that will not be possible if they do not enjoy natural poise.

Brian is a comedian who does the London circuit performing his own wry brand of humour. A tall man, he tended to stoop, and consequently suffered from back pain. He also had the tendency to round his shoulders, and didn't make much of a visual impact on stage. However, by having regular sessions with me, his whole demeanour has changed, and while still being relaxed and great fun, he's enjoying not having backache or postural problems. His stature has improved and he now has more stage presence.

The demands of concert performance can create enormous stress and they can even affect our performance. The importance of being free of unnecessary tension and well poised cannot be overstated. If we can make any improvements to our overall co-ordination, they will filter through to enhance our ability to perform, while also helping us cope well with the pressure of the occasion.

I once got a phone call from a gentleman patron of the arts, asking me if I could help an international concert pianist whom he was particularly keen to support. Rosalind apparently had a piano recital on London's South Bank scheduled for the following week, but she was suffering from stress that was affecting her playing. When we met, I could see that she had some tendencies to hunch over the keyboard, shortening her stature, and to stiffen her neck and shoulders a little, which in turn affected her playing. These tendencies were also interfering with her breathing and causing stress.

Rosalind was undoubtedly an accomplished performer, and had made a successful career on the international concert platform, but her physical tendencies weren't helping her make the absolute best of herself or her performance. We had daily sessions for the few days remaining before the concert, and she responded well, quickly becoming freer while also beginning to carry herself with a more upright stature. Her breathing improved as a result of the release and freeing up of her ribs and this helped her sense of calmness.

I went along to the concert with my partner and we thoroughly enjoyed the evening's recital, and also had a chance to chat with the gentleman who had referred her. I later got a letter from him, thanking me for my help, and saying that he'd never heard her play so well.

Control and co-ordination

Accuracy of movement, spontaneity, speed and agility all come from our co-ordination. With over 400 muscles in our bodies, we need them all to work together in a highly synchronised manner. This synchronisation is really put to the test when we have to perform in sport, music, dance or public speaking. It is during these moments when we are under pressure that our co-ordination will either see us through well, or let us down. And of course, for most of us the main influences that affect our co-ordination are the unnecessary tension and habits. They are with us 100 per cent of the time, so it's obvious that if we want to improve our performance we've got to attend to our habits permanently.

Rod is a competitive breakdancer and practises several hours daily to perfect various moves. He explained to me how it can take up to a year to learn just one new movement, where the speed, balance and co-ordination necessary require ultimate synchronisation. Head and shoulder spins at six revolutions a second and leg scissor cuts on the floor are examples of the finesse required for his performance. Rod found that an improvement in his overall co-ordination and balance helped his agility and precise movement. In other words, his performance was bettered, not just by practising dance, but by attending to his overall condition.

Being an actor requires you to be in a 'neutral' state and free of habits because they will interfere with your ability to enact different roles. Actors need to be adaptable and able to change their whole demeanour so that they can consciously take on characteristics that are not their own, in order to portray a believable character, be it on stage, film or TV. If they are trapped in their own habits, then their ability to do this will be severely limited.

Many drama schools and music academies now incorporate into their normal curriculum regular lessons in the Alexander Technique, a method now so widely known that most performers are not only aware of it, but have probably already had sessions to help them professionally. These teach the individual to become more aware of their habits and learn how to overcome them and be more consciously in control.

F.M. Alexander, the founder of the technique, was himself a successful actor in Sydney and Melbourne during the late nineteenth century before severe vocal problems almost forced him to give up his career. As the vocal specialists and doctors were unable to help him, he felt compelled to investigate his condition for himself. He went through a lengthy period of experimentation and close observation of how he used his body, with the aid of mirrors to see himself from every angle. It was at this time that he discovered the importance of Inhibition as a means of preventing the wrong use of himself.

Eventually he found that he had not only resolved his vocal problems, but had also improved his stature. He became well known for his important discoveries in how the body functions and his help was sought not only by many actors, but doctors started referring patients with breathing problems to him. The methods that he evolved to help himself as an actor have since become known as the Alexander Technique and can help people overcome a wide range of problems.

Catherine enjoys amateur dramatics. She has a growing family and now has more time for herself and wants to pursue her interest in acting. However, she feels that her posture lets her down as she has quite a pronounced stoop that characterises her in no uncertain terms. When we met, she was quite bent over, with rather narrowed shoulders and a frown that didn't bear any relation to her mood, but was simply a habit.

We had regular one-to-one sessions for quite some time, and I encouraged her to lie down on the floor at home daily for ten minutes at a time, in the manner described in the last chapter.

Catherine now finds that she is so much more upright and no longer needs to pull her head backwards with tension in order to see where she's going. Her shoulders have opened out, giving her more breadth and bearing, the concerned frown has reduced considerably and her breathing improved. She hopes that her new upright poise will allow her to play a broader range of roles in her local amateur theatre company.

SPORT

Have you ever been in awe watching an acrobat walk across a tightrope only using a long pole to help balance? The wire is only about an inch in diameter, yet, although it moves from side to side, the acrobat will go with the movement, compensating and readjusting their weight with split-second timing. Obviously their reflexes are wonderfully quick and their sense of balance finely tuned. Maybe as a child you walked along the top of a narrow garden wall, and you could probably run along it without falling off because you were free in your joints and your balance was good. Well, this is the same agility that we still need as adults if we're going to be successful at sport.

Let's create a new set of conditions for our acrobat and ask them to wear a neck splint, which sounds terrible, but is simply a neck support that prevents all movement by holding their head and neck in a fixed position in relation to their shoulders. Ask them to walk the wire again wearing the neck splint, and they'd find that they wouldn't be able to maintain their balance and would fall off after only two or three strides. This illustrates the importance of keeping a free neck and allowing the weight of our head to balance freely on the top of our spine. This may seem like an extreme example, yet this is the sort of condition that most of us have all the time. We are interfering with the balance of our heads by tightening our neck muscles in a habitual way, all day long.

Importance of head balance

Since an adult head usually weighs the equivalent of about five bags of sugar, between 4 and 6 kilos, it has a tremendous influence on the balance of our whole body. In a healthy person, and you can easily see this in two-year-old children, the head balances very freely, and it will wobble back and forth so that the weight compensates depending on the angle of the body underneath. The head weight acts as part of our whole balancing mechanism. If we tighten our muscles and lock our head position solid on our neck, it will prevent our head from righting itself with subtle and subconscious adjustments, and we will become unstable on our feet. Neck tension is not just the cause of neck pain and discomfort, but it actually affects the way we perform. It has a much greater effect on our bodies than we might at first realise.

Neck tension reduces the sensitivity of the small but highly important suboccipital muscles deep underneath the skull. These little muscles work in conjunction with our vestibular mechanism of the inner ear and our eyes to send feedback information to the brain about our position and our overall balance. In other words, they help to tell the brain where we are in space. As a sports person, we need these functions to be working 100 per cent.

Running

Running is a bipedal action as much as walking, but the movement is different and our balance changes. Fundamentally we need to be free in all our joints and lengthening in stature as much as for any other occasion. So if possible we should free our neck, send our heads upwards and allow our back to lengthen and widen as we run, making sure that we don't make any effort to lengthen, only thinking it. However, with the momentum of running, our upright poise will lean slightly forwards to maintain balance, but it's important that we don't overdo this as we'll get off balance. Keeping our attention on our head going upwards will help our body adjust appropriately without us trying to calculate the degree of lean. As we tire it is common for us to start leaning further forwards and begin to shorten in stature. In other words, we can start to stoop, run into the ground, plod heavily and get off balance. This is a contraction of our stature and the excessive tension involved works against us. We must keep ourselves free and going up. If we're so tired that we're collapsing it would be a good idea to stop or walk a bit to recover our poise before recommencing. A process of little and often will extend our abilities so that we can run longer and faster without causing ourselves harm.

The actions of the legs are also important. In the process of walking the heel should touch the ground in front of us first and as we travel over this leg, there will be a rolling action of the foot so that our toes eventually push off the ground for the next stride. It's rather like pedalling a bike. However, when we're running, our body weight moves forward so we do not come down on our heels as this would slow us down, but run more on the balls of our feet. As part of overall leg action the knee will be bending and should point in the general direction in which we're running but angled slightly so that the knee goes out over the big toe. The knee will splay out slightly but no more than the feet are. If we are knocking our knees, inappropriate tensions in our legs are pulling inwards. We should think of sending our knees forwards in the direction we are running and allow them to go over our toes. The action of our legs is governed to a high degree on whether our neck is free and if we are lengthening and widening. It's therefore important that we send our head upwards as we run, which will also help to avoid the hollowing and tightening of our lower back that causes tight compression.

Good running shoes will help absorb the shock on our joints when we're on hard surfaces but soft ground such as grass is preferable to pavements as it's kinder to our system. Uneven ground will also vary the way our feet fall with every stride so keeping our joints more flexible and avoiding repetitive actions that cause strain and deterioration. Roads and pavements are modern inventions that are far removed from the natural environment of rough terrain that our ancient ancestors would have enjoyed. So it's worth finding a park to run in, and go off track!

Running is a great activity but like all things needs to be done well if unnecessary strain is to be avoided. Practise for short spells while improving your running style to avoid excessive tiredness that will undermine your efforts.

Ruth enjoys running in the country. She does 6 to 8 miles at weekends, and in the summer evenings after work. However, although she enjoyed the outdoor experience and exertion, she found that she tended to get an aching lower back and stiff knees. The situation seemed to be getting worse, and she was worried that she would have to give up her regular runs. She couldn't understand why an activity that is considered to be healthy and athletic could cause her so much discomfort and felt that maybe she had a physical limitation and simply wasn't up to it.

Having met Ruth, and watched how she moved, I could see that she had the distinct tendency to pull her head backwards off balance while also arching her back. Ruth also tended to lean forwards quite considerably, so that her body weight was falling in front of her as she walked or ran. She came to me for a short course of Alexander Technique sessions during which she became more aware of her balance and gradually started to apply the principles of loosening, lengthening and widening to her running, first for short distances, then longer. She reported back to me that her lower back no longer ached and her knees were freer. Ruth was no longer wasting effort in her unnecessary tensions and the efficiency of her running improved so that she could go further and faster, with seemingly less effort.

Being 'present'

In sport, as with anything else, it is important that we are completely 'in the moment'. Anticipation is an important aspect of all sporting activity, for example anticipating the actions of our opponent or the play of the ball. But as far as our mental and physical condition is concerned, we need to be well poised, balanced and free to move in any direction at any time. This means that we mustn't be holding the posture of two seconds ago when we actually need to be adapting to the game moment by moment. We mustn't be stiffening our muscles in such a way that the tension interferes with our fluid movement. When playing the ball, we mustn't rush and take our eyes off the ball. We should attend to how we're performing the stroke or kick and let the end result take care of itself. Yes, we can envisage or visualise playing the ball superbly, and winning the match or race, but our attention should be on ensuring that all our physical functioning, second by second, is performing to its best. Improvements in our poise and balance will also help our awareness to anticipate the opponent's actions too. If we can keep our neck free of tension, we are far more likely to succeed at everything we do.

Louise is a swimmer and particularly enjoys the freedom of being in water and the invigoration of the whole process. However she tended to swim with her head out of the water while doing the breast stroke and she wanted to make some improvements. I explained to Louise that when she has her head above water, it is in fact pulled right back at a severe angle to her torso. This is similar to standing upright and pointing her face at the ceiling all the time. By doing so, she was squashing her neck vertebrae and discs. When she's swimming like this, she is actually coming backwards with her head and shortening her spine when she wants to swim forwards. If she could swim with her head in the water facing the floor of the pool, she would be leading with the crown of her head, which would encourage a lengthening of her spine during the movement. This is a quality we all need to function well. She would then come up to breathe by the use of her arms. Louise practised this and found that her stroke improved, she made far less effort, her speed increased and she was able to swim further without getting tired or breathless.

Swimming is a great activity that gets the whole body moving, the breathing and circulation working while also exercising your muscles. As the water is supporting your body weight there is no pressure on the joints, so there are lots of opportunities to be expansive and free as we swim. If you are interested in improving your swimming technique, you may like to look at the Shaw Method of Swimming which is based on the principles of the Alexander Technique. Further details will be found in the back of this book.

A golfer who intends to go professional came to me about his posture. He had accidentally strained himself and this was causing him to stiffen throughout his body. He hoped that some sessions with me might help improve his condition. During his course of sessions with me John has made good progress in the use of himself, becoming much freer and more upright. He stands taller, but as a result of us working on his co-ordination in movement and when he bends, he finds that his golf game has improved. John feels that not only have the painful symptoms of his strain become less, he is playing his best ever golf. He tells me that he is finding it so easy and natural to make a swing and his strokes are more accurate. John is very excited about his future as a professional golfer.

We all want to be sufficiently fit to perform our sport well, so we exercise or work out. However, it will be helpful if we don't just *do* the exercises, but also pay attention to *how* we do them. We should maintain awareness of ourselves during the exercises to ensure that we don't cause harm by straining.

We should also endeavour to keep our necks free, and maintain a tall and broad stature. Tired and worked muscles have the tendency to shorten and contract, so stretches are likely to be beneficial. When we've finished, it is a good idea to lie down on the floor and perform the semi-supine procedure as described in chapter 10 to help release our muscles of their tension and restore ourselves to our full height. If we want to do gym work, I would recommend a 'little and often' approach rather than one long session per week which may cause damage.

Tuition

It's important when being coached in sport, or any other activity, that you don't develop new bad habits as you learn. If you pick up bad habits from the outset by watching and copying inexpert players, they will be much harder to get rid of than if you'd started out properly in the first place. This may seem obvious, but it's important from a postural point of view. Make sure when choosing your coach or instructor that they demonstrate good postural use of themselves.

Exercise: Lengthen while running

When you're running (or doing any sport) it's important that you lengthen in stature rather than shorten. Lengthening helps your musculature to co-ordinate better. You will run faster and with less effort if you are going up with your head and lengthening in stature.

Free your neck muscles and allow your head to balance freely on the top of your spine at a height between your ears by letting your nose drop a centimetre. Allow your head to 'teeter'.

Now think of your head going upwards and of your back length-ening and widening. Don't make any effort to lengthen – just think it. This is the quality we all need for our body to function efficiently. When you're running, think these thoughts all the time. The sequence of thoughts is important.

1. Free your neck.
2. Send (think) your head forwards and upwards.
3. Think of your back lengthening.
4. Think of your back widening.
5. Send your knees forwards and away.

See chapter 6 for further guidelines.

Any performer, be it on stage, TV, film, music, dance, or sport needs their body and mind to be synchronised to the highest level. Any slight interference in their co-ordination will affect their performance. For all of us who want to make the most of ourselves, it's essential to ensure that we have minimised any interference to our co-ordination by taking control of our postural habits.

It's reassuring to remember that we all have it within ourselves to perform better at virtually anything we do. Your poise has a direct influence on your performance. You can revive your natural poise now by taking more conscious control.

IN A NUTSHELL

- Everybody is required to perform at some time: at work, in difficult situations and sometimes socially – not just in sport or the arts.
- Our postural habits will affect our sports performance unless we work on eliminating them during our normal daily life.
- If we keep our neck free and improve our co-ordination we will help ourselves perform with more accuracy and control.
- Work on the process rather than the end result.
- When learning sport it's important to have a good example to copy.

HELPFUL TIPS

1. Improve your posture and voice in daily life so that when you perform you don't bring your old habits with you.
2. Free your neck as often as you can during your daily life. This helps you minimise the effects of your bad postural habits so when you really want to perform your best, you are not so disadvantaged by them.
3. When running or doing any sport, free your neck and think of your head going upwards to lengthen your spine; by doing so you will become more dynamic and athletic.

Sex Appeal

When it comes down to it, what we really want is sex. At least, most of us want to be beautiful, and to feel good and attractive in ourselves, but also to know that we're desirable to others. It's part of nature, and if we are women, we devise ways of enhancing our appeal such as by wearing high heels, and we feel the need for a slim waist, a hairdo, a make-over, a tooth job, and in extreme cases a Botoxed, implanted, uplifted, lipo'd and reconstructed body! Although most of us won't consider such extreme lengths to increase our appeal, we *will* give attention to personal grooming, and may wear make-up too.

As we saw in the previous chapter, we perform in all kinds of different situations, and being on a date or social occasion is no different. For instance most of us like to look and feel our best, particularly when we go out to dinner with friends, or to a function, the theatre or a concert. It's nice to take our time getting ready so that when we're with others, we too will feel special. Naturally, we like to be attractive to whoever we're with, be it our husband, wife or partner or even in a business situation. If we're at a conference or important meeting we want to look the part, to be smart, appear professional, sophisticated, successful and at ease within ourselves. We want to make a good impression, and we want people to like us. This is all very normal and most of us will give attention to helping ourselves appear at our best.

In marketing it is said that an advert is 'sexy'. In other words it has appeal and 'come on'. It makes us want to buy the product. When looking at someone we may think that they have nice features, or a beautiful figure or lovely clothes, but it is rare that those aspects alone will draw us. If we are attracted to someone it's usually because we're drawn to something on a deeper and more subconscious level. These people are giving off something more subtle that we find appealing, whether it's their energy or their aura that attracts us.

When we prepare to go out we attend to the grooming considerations and choose attractive clothes before we head for the door. We often only concern ourselves with our outer appearance. We decorate the outside of us; what we feel people see. We don't necessarily address what people sense.

There are some things that we may not consider which have an equally powerful effect on the way we present ourselves. Some aspects of ourselves are so much part of us that if we were aware of them, we might feel that there isn't much that can be done to change. We're talking about our physical demeanour, and not just the cosmetic treatments and considerations that we give to our exterior. It's what's going on inside us that can have an enormous effect. We're talking about the essence of ourselves.

We normally find certain qualities in people very attractive and sexy. Personality of course is one. Reasonable fitness is another, but also if they appear upright, relaxed, cool and confident within themselves; if only we could have that relaxed, emotionally centred and calm, self-assured quality too! If we could also move with nimbleness and fluidity, have open-ness across our chest, have clear skin, be relaxed in our facial muscles, smile, and look calm and happy and have a gorgeous voice. These qualities are the most natural in the world, yet to find someone displaying them all tends to be a rare experience. I would also suggest that these are the qualities that more of us could have, but do not, only because we are preventing ourselves from having them. In other words, we are not loose because we are stiffening, we have dry skin partly because we don't breathe efficiently, we frown and tighten our facial muscles and we may not drink enough water. We are stooped and pulling ourselves down because we've lost our sense of balance and developed a whole load of habits to compensate. But these aspects also have much deeper influences. Our whole health and wellbeing is undermined.

Our inner organs may be under stress too, partly by our slouch that compresses them, but also because of emotional as well as dietary reasons. Our system may be under strain, and this will affect our whole demeanour. We cannot be truly relaxed and calm when our system is under stress. I'm not talking about stress at work or any other external situation, although our ability to cope in these circumstances is also affected by how well co-ordinated and balanced we are. No, I'm referring to the general functioning of our whole 'self' that can be under significant strain, and this will be expressed through our energy and will affect how we interact with others. And although we may feign to be happy, calm and wonderful, something deeper is giving off other signals that conflict with our manner. So there is dissonance in our portrayal of ourselves, which is discomforting to those with whom we interact. We're not sexy. We don't have that special something that can only exist when we're truly at one with ourselves.

Sex appeal comes from within

It's possible to meet people who one might say are not traditionally beautiful, in fact they may be positively unattractive in certain ways, be it their features, figure, hair or clothing. But despite this they may also be enormously sexy or sensuous. They can have a wonderful sexual appeal because they are radiating something very special. They exude this quality from within. Indeed someone like this can be far sexier than another with the perfect figure, sculpted features and stunning clothes. The latter person may be sending out a conflict of statements: she may not be really calm, centred and content within herself and this is what we subconsciously pick up. This conflict makes us uneasy.

So how do we get this wonderful inner quality? We must attend to our diet, our water consumption, our general lifestyle. We should attend to our posture and ensure that we truly are in balance, well poised, breathing well, free in all our joints so that we can move easily. As we've said, our emotions are enormously affected by our physical condition and by improving our posture we will certainly change how we feel about ourselves and how we come over to others.

However, it's not important only for making us feel confident and sexy: good poise enhances your health, and can make you look slimmer and taller and more elegant too. So we're going to look at that in more detail in a moment.

IN A NUTSHELL

- **True sexiness comes from within and is a quality that we exude.**
- **We can change our style, hair and make-up, but in order to be truly cool and sexy, we need to pay attention to our posture, diet, fluid intake and our breathing.**
- **By attending to our posture we can become more upright, freer and able to move with fluidity, all aspects that can help us feel younger, be fitter and sexier.**

HELPFUL TIPS

1. Minimise the stressful situations in your life so that you can relax.
2. Attend to the obvious, such as get enough sleep, eat nourishing food and drink plenty of water.
3. Improve your posture so that you are in better balance, more centred and breathing well.

Remember that these are the things that will have a deep effect on your persona and how you come over to others.

Facial fixation and frowning

When it comes to winning new friends, attracting lovers and interacting with people, our faces play a major role. Yet our face may be conveying negative messages to those we meet without us even being aware of it. Problems include furrowing the brow, frowning subconsciously, as well as other types of 'facial freezing' where we hold tension in the cheeks and the jowls. Not only are such gestures or habits liable to be interpreted as 'unfriendly' signals but they are also ageing and unhealthy. A fixed and unmoving face is likely to be linked to physical rigidity, unhealthy postural tensions, as well as giving a false indication of our attitude and personality.

While we may not all want the rubber face of a TV comic, it's pleasing if our face is free and expressive. Frowning itself is not a problem when it's part of a wide range of facial expressions, but it can become a problem if facial muscle tension becomes a habit, fixed like a mask. Freely moving facial expressions are an important aspect of communication so we should avoid any treatments that are both toxic and intended to 'freeze' these muscles. We're all attracted to people who are open and expressive; faces that are paralysed are very unappealing. Look at those of young children, laughing and jollying away and letting us know exactly how they feel. The tensions in our body, too, are often expressed in our face. Freeing up our posture so that we're loose and expansive will also help the free expression of our face, and vice versa.

Improvements to our breathing will probably have the greatest benefit on our complexion, along with drinking adequate amounts of water. Our skin will improve as freeing up the muscles will help improve blood circulation, deliver more oxygen to the skin and reduce toxins. This in turn will lead to a clearer and more translucent complexion. Relaxing our facial muscles can also help reduce neck, jaw and shoulder tension and indeed improve our whole poise.

We can help ourselves by allowing our face to be relaxed and 'open' like the stage curtains at the theatre. Think open and wide: don't stretch it. We can also allow our lips to be free, not pursed or tightened. Many mouth lines are caused by puckering and pursing so allow your lips to be soft, wide and voluptuous. Remember that hair lines give us character, and we shouldn't necessarily try to eliminate these. We like character! We can help ourselves be healthier and more expressive if we are able to leave it all alone. And by doing so, your friends may think that you're just back from a great holiday!

Power of laughter

'I like the laughter that opens the lips and the heart – that shows at the same time pearls and the soul,' said Victor Hugo. Laughing is a very healthy exertion and sometimes referred to as 'jogging for the insides'. Apparently, children can laugh between 400 and 600 times each day, but adults rarely laugh at all, and at best just for a few moments. Yet it's a real stress-buster! While stress itself is known to suppress our immune system, laughter apparently helps boost the immune system. It also helps to free up the whole body to improve our poise.

Laughter is an activity that is unique to humans, but many of us rarely allow ourselves this most wholesome and healthy of experiences. We would do ourselves the world of good if we could learn to smile and laugh again. To open up our throats and mouths and let out a good hearty laugh does wonders for our health, mood and sense of wellbeing. It's an uplifting experience that's connected to our whole poise and gets our insides bobbing up and down. It frees us up physically while also creating good hormones such as endorphins and neurotransmitters, and decreases levels of stress hormones such as cortisol and adrenaline. And if you can't find anything funny to laugh about, 'manufacture' a laugh. The body apparently responds to pretend laughter in the same way as real laughter. If you just do it, you'll soon start laughing naturally anyway. Use every opportunity you can find to have a laugh or at least to smile. And if your friends think that you've entirely lost it and gone crazy, they're the ones missing out. From my own experience, I recommend a minimum of five minutes of laughter daily, in small amounts spread throughout the day. Do it for a week and see how you feel. Go on: it's good to laugh!

Smiling too brings with it many of the health benefits mentioned above. It also has a beneficial effect on our facial expression and our whole poise. The smile is an upward movement of the facial muscles that can contribute to the healthy working of our postural mechanism. As bipeds, we need to be going upwards in order for our muscle co-ordination to support us effectively. Smiling not only helps make us attractive, it's good for our health. 'Smile and the whole world smiles with you.'

But, of course, laughter isn't the only sound we make from our mouth. Our voice is often an overlooked aspect of being sexy and appealing, yet it is a hugely important means of expressing ourselves. I feel that having a good speaking voice is so important that I've devoted the next chapter entirely to showing how you can improve the sound of your voice so that every time you speak, you can stop people in their tracks.

Look a million dollars

Imagine that you've got a hot date this evening. You've groomed yourself beautifully and selected a stunning outfit by your favourite designer. When you put it on, you're suddenly looking at the real you in the mirror and part of your mental image of yourself is shattered. Your posture is letting you down. Suddenly your expensive outfit doesn't look quite the price you paid for it. If we were able to stand tall and upright in a relaxed manner, then our clothes would hang perfectly in the way that they were envisaged by the designer. And if we were to have such posture, we would be able to wear just about any clothes we liked and still look a million dollars.

Exercise: Thinking tall

This procedure is based on the principles explained in chapter 6.

In order to maintain your proper slim shape, you should free your neck and send your head upwards. Do this by thinking only. Also think of your back lengthening. As already discussed, your body is very springy and it's probable that your full height is taller than you normally experience. It's important that you don't make any physical effort to achieve this as you will only get stiff. Think loose

---

> and tall as often as you can. As described before, you are tapping
> into the natural instinct you have for good poise that you've had
> from birth. It's just that you're now encouraging it consciously.

It's very difficult to look in the mirror and not physically do something about our dissatisfaction, like pull our shoulders backwards, or brace our backs so we appear more upright, or suck our tummy in so it looks a bit flatter. When we do this, you can imagine all the tension we're creating to try to correct what we think is the outer failing. Do we see young children pulling their shoulders back or making a huge effort to be upright? You might say that they don't have sticky-out tummies or a slouch. But their poise is happening naturally, because they haven't yet developed any bad habits.

If we've become rounded in the shoulders it's because we're pulling them forwards out of alignment. If we don't tighten the muscles that pull our shoulders forwards in the first place, they won't be displaced in such a way. It's clear that it doesn't make sense to create a whole lot of tension elsewhere to correct something that is already tense in the wrong way. We should release the tension that's pulling them out of their natural alignment and restore our natural poise by using the principles in this book. To help your shoulders, perform the semi-supine procedure in chapter 10.

Cindy was getting married in three months and wanted to improve her posture for when she walked down the aisle. She wanted the day to be perfect. Although Cindy was quite tall and very attractive, she felt that her hunched shoulders let her down and wondered if the Alexander Technique could help her. We had regular sessions and when the day came, she was more than delighted as her shape had changed quite dramatically. The stoop had all but disappeared, she was walking taller and more upright and her waist seemed slimmer. To top it all, her wedding dress that had been cut so that it came to the floor now hung freely and her beautiful silver shoes became visible as she walked.

A broad male chest

Men have commented that they would like to have a broader chest and shoulders. Well, we can puff ourselves up like a pigeon in front of the mirror, but when we release and breathe out again, everything deflates. Working out in a gym may also have failed; muscle bulk is one thing, but a broader frame is another. Yet when we learn to release much of the unnecessary tension around our chest and shoulders, they have the opportunity of expanding to their proper width. Some men who have had lessons in the Alexander Technique have seen their chest expand by as much as 2 inches. One particular young man who was having lessons from me came in one day and mentioned that he'd met a friend at the weekend he hadn't seen for several months, who had asked him if he was working out in a gym because he looked so much broader. His friend was surprised to learn that it was because he was in the middle of a course of Alexander Technique lessons.

Slimmer waist without dieting

We may feel that it would be lovely to be a bit slimmer and taller. If we are collapsing in front by slouching so that our tummy sticks out, it would make far more sense to correct the overall co-ordination of the body so that we can lengthen and learn to sustain natural and upright tall poise all day without effort. Sucking our guts in is harmful to our breathing, digestion, bowel movements and reproductive organs. It is also an unnatural effort that we can't sustain.

If we improve our co-ordination our back will be more supported and consequently our waist and tummy, without dieting or losing any weight, can appear slimmer. I've had many clients who have either commented themselves or have had friends comment on how slim they look, but they haven't necessarily lost any weight!

One lady in her forties who came to me for Alexander Technique lessons some time ago was so chuffed with her changes that she started tucking her blouse inside the waistband of her trousers because she now felt that she had a waist again. She hadn't lost any weight as such, but her co-ordination had changed sufficiently so that she was naturally standing taller at her full height more of the time rather than slumping down into herself, which had previously given her the appearance of being dumpy. She now feels very pleased and proud of her new figure.

Wearing high heels

Being a bloke who was born halfway through the last century I had personal experience in the early 1970s of platform shoes and I wore them with relish. Red and blue, patterned ones that were *high*. Difficult to walk and dance in, but, boy, was I the bee's knees! However the effect of these on our feet and our walking is nothing compared to the extreme tilt of the foot that high heels create. I have to say I'm glad that I don't wear this type of shoe any more. But if you wear high heels, I'd like to offer a few comments.

High heels throw the weight of your body forwards by tilting your feet, and the higher the heel, the more the tilt. This may be fine if you're able to adjust your balance to cope, but many of you may have postural tensions and habits that are already throwing you a bit off balance and high-heeled shoes can make it worse. If you've got the tendency to stiffen your legs and ankles, which many of us do, then your body will not be able to 'right itself' and adjust appropriately to help you balance. This will then make you stiffen your hips and probably throw your body weight forwards. You may compensate for this by leaning backwards from the waist, creating a lot of tension in your back that will shorten your stature. Excessive curvature of your spine may be brought about by unwanted muscle tension. This causes compression of the discs between the vertebrae and puts harmful pressure on nerves.

High heels also affect the muscles and joints in your feet. When wearing them, the weight of your body is being thrust downwards and forwards through your foot to put excessive pressure on the joints behind your toes. This can cause serious foot problems including bunions, hard skin and even trapped nerves. It is important that the shoes you wear are not too tight but also offer support throughout the whole foot to spread the load.

So what should we do?

Well, I'm often asked if wearing high heels is bad, and if it is okay to wear them. And although my instinct is to say that it's better for your health not to wear high heels, that is not terribly helpful because we all like to look elegant and sexy and there will be times when you want to wear them. So my answer is, yes, it's okay to wear them, but don't have them too high, and don't do it all the time. Keep them for special occasions when you really feel they're indispensable! And when you do wear them, it's important that you are aware of your balance and ensure that you're free enough to allow your body to compensate.

Exercise: Balancing in high heels

To improve your balance when wearing high heels try the following.

First, in stocking feet, perform the Balancing exercise from p52. Find your upright balance so that the weight of your body is going down through your ankles. The alignment of your body should roughly be so that your ears are over your shoulders, your shoulders are over your hips, and your hips are over your ankles. Do this without stiffening. Think of being loose.

Now free your neck, think of sending your head upwards so that

---

you are encouraging your back to lengthen. Do not make any physical effort. Just think it.

Now put on your favourite high heels and do the same exercise. You will immediately feel that your body weight is thrown forwards, but it's important that you allow your ankles to be free so that your body can adjust to become vertical. Again, think of your head going upwards and your back lengthening and widening. But only think it. Do not make any physical effort. This is important.

When you walk, it's essential that you don't lean forwards, but maintain upright, loose poise the whole time.

Wearing high heels can have the effect of shortening your hamstrings in the back of your legs. This can be quite a handicap if you try to bend down to pick something up off the floor, and you may find it impossible without going on to your toes and your heels coming up. Ideally we should be able to bend our knees and go down towards the floor while keeping our feet flat on the floor. Tight and shortened hamstrings are also detrimental to your whole posture and ability to move freely. It will be helpful if you can encourage your hamstrings to lengthen and the following exercise can do this. However, there are dangers in stretching too much, so take care always to avoid straining. Follow the guidelines carefully.

Exercise: Lengthening the hamstrings

To help lengthen your hamstrings you can perform an exercise that is often used by horse riders to improve their abilities in dressage.

Stand on a step or staircase and use a handrail for support. Bring your feet back so that your heels overhang the step and you are standing on your toes and the pads behind your toes. Your foot will be half on and half off the step. Now allow your heels to drop downwards by a centimetre or two so that they are lower than the level of the step. You will feel the stretch down the backs of your legs. It is important that you don't do this for too long or so extremely that you damage your tendons. Start off by doing it for a few seconds or so, and increase slowly to one minute, then up to five or ten minutes per day. Be gentle and only increase the stretch if you can do so comfortably. If you feel any pain or discomfort you must stop immediately. Seek advice from a doctor or physiotherapist if you are in any doubt about doing this exercise. Over time it is likely that your hamstrings will lengthen and this will help you maintain more upright poise.

We are naturally drawn to beautiful qualities because deep down we probably recognise them as being indicative of a suitably healthy 'mate' for reproduction. As we get older, it seems that we are almost expected to lose these qualities as a matter of course through the ageing process. But just because most people display such ageing conditions doesn't mean that they are natural. Through my work, I have found that we tend to expect these conditions because they're so common, but in fact the vast proportion of us are making ourselves age faster than we should. By taking some corrective action, many of these 'symptoms' or conditions can be reduced, so that in the law of averages we can look and feel younger than our years would suggest. I shall discuss ageing again in chapter 14.

By becoming more aware of ourselves and learning how to overcome our habitual tendencies, we can have a dramatic effect not only on our health and wellbeing, but also in how we are perceived.

So when we're thinking about how we could improve our image, and make the most of ourselves professionally or socially, or when we would like to appear sexier than we do, let's just remember that there are certain deep and fundamental things that we really can change about ourselves if we choose to. In my experience, it is possible for everyone to make changes to their lives in how they feel, how they look and to their health. These sorts of changes cannot be manufactured overnight or just for the important occasion when we want to look our best. By taking a decision now, that we would like to change, we can get the ball rolling and start helping ourselves from today.

IN A NUTSHELL

- **Relax your face and allow your full range of expression.**
- **Laughing can improve your health and wellbeing.**
- **Smile.**
- **Wearing high heels isn't ideal, but we can help**

avoid causing ourselves harm if we are aware of our balance and remain free and upright.

- Collapsing in stature makes you look smaller and fatter than you really are.
- Having a good speaking voice can be enormously sexy and appealing.

HELPFUL TIPS

1. Take every opportunity you can to laugh.
2. When wearing high heels ensure that you're not leaning forwards. Be free in your ankles and neck and allow your body to adjust itself to compensate for the tilt. Your body should be upright and not arching in the waist.
3. Don't hold your tummy in as this affects the working of your internal organs.
4. General exercise (housework is great!) will be of help in keeping you fit and toned.
5. Improve your poise to improve your appeal.

Your Gorgeous Voice

Haven't you noticed sometimes how wonderful some people look: they're healthy, long-limbed, dressed immaculately, sexy, with beautiful features, and then, when you truly think they've come from heaven, they open their mouth to speak and your illusions drop through the floor? 'Oh, God! What a terrible voice!'

It's amusing to think how we attend to all sorts of things relating to our appearance such as dress and grooming, but we somehow forget all about our voice. Yet it's one of the most effective and influential means of communication and presenting ourselves. When people say first impressions count, we've got to consider the sound of our voice, because a beautiful one can send tingles down the spine, and get everyone listening. A good speaking voice is not only sexy and appealing, but it can bring many benefits in business, to win contracts, sway discussions and bring authoritative power to the speaker. The voice is a tool that we all have but few capitalise on our abilities to use it effectively. It's possible for all of us to enhance our voice in a way that can have a positive influence on our lives. This chapter is going to look at this more deeply.

I know someone who was constantly being telephoned by a young woman whom he'd met once at a party and who wanted to talk for ages, but never to meet him for a date. He got the impression that she fancied him, but when, after many calls, he pushed the idea of meeting, it transpired that it was only the sound of his voice that she loved, and she didn't much care for him in other ways. What a disappointment for him, but how nice to have such a voice that makes people drool!

Some performers have wonderful voices. I'm thinking of people such as Lindsay Duncan, Fenella Fielding, Katharine Hepburn, Alan Rickman, Christopher Lee, Nick Nolte, Barry White, and who can ignore that great Scots voice of Sean Connery. Some of you may also remember such actors as Yul Brynner and James Mason: all voices that have a magic, and can mesmerise without you even seeing their faces.

We 'make' our voice

People remark that so-and-so has a good voice, or you'll hear some people comment, 'I don't have a good voice.' Yet the voice is not something in itself, like a separate and identifiable part of us, but the *product* of us, personally. The voice doesn't exist until we make it! But it is the manner in which we make it that can have such an effect on the way we sound. We may all be different in terms of height, shape, breadth, weight, age and sex, and it's true that these variations influence the sound of our voice. But these are not the only factors.

If we listen to an inexperienced violinist playing some Mozart, it may sound rather scratchy and squawky, and out of tune. You might say that they don't yet play the violin very well. On the other hand, if you hear a virtuoso performer playing the same piece, it will sound magical, with resonance, and a soft, smooth, rich tone, which soars like a bird and you'd say that they play the violin beautifully. Our voice, too, can be considered as an instrument in the same way as the violin. It's just that our instrument is ourselves. We 'play' ourselves to make our voice, and the manner in which we play it will determine what sort of sound we produce.

If we've got a thin and squeaky voice then we're not using what we've got to our best advantage. The same could be said if we're husky and breathy, or tight and strained, or if we stammer. It's often said how nice it is to hear a good voice: rich in tone, clear in the upper harmonics, liquid and smooth, unforced and unstrained, well articulated and modulated in pitch. This would be when the performer is 'playing his instrument well'.

Our vocal mechanism is something that we use just as much as our legs to walk or our hands to write. It is a part of our body that needs to be used appropriately for it to perform at its best, and will not do so if we misuse it. If we don't have a good voice, it is because we don't make it well. And if we change the way that we do it, we will enjoy a change to the way it sounds. It's as simple as that, or not, as the case may be. Because when we speak or sing, we activate all our physical and habitual tendencies, and they have a direct bearing on how we function and the sound we make.

An opera singer had some sessions with a view to improving his performance and vocal power. Once again, it was important to refine his sense of balance and gain release of tensions around his neck and torso. He is a tall man, and very large in his chest as a result of a lot of singing training. However his tendency was to stiffen, rather than allow everything to be free and relaxed. At the end of each session we'd have a few minutes of gentle vocal work such as humming to free up the system, and then he'd sing just a few notes. And on every occasion without fail, he would startle himself and exclaim, 'Listen to that!' when he heard how dramatically his voice had changed during the forty-minute session. We hadn't been working on his voice, but by fine-tuning his balance and co-ordination his vocal mechanism could function with less interference and the results were immediate.

Your poise affects your voice

Being a biped on only two feet, rather than four as we've already discussed, has an enormous influence on our functioning as we've no other means of support. We can be standing, coping with gravity, but if we're not in balance and consequently stiffening our musculature, then these conditions will affect our voice. We need the efficient functioning of our whole body in order to make a beautiful sound through our mouth. It doesn't matter whether you are a manager presenting a business proposal, a singer in the church choir, a rap artist, a chairman of your company speaking to shareholders, or a brother giving a speech at your sister's wedding. We still need all our equipment to be functioning well, and that means that we mustn't interfere with it.

We may have specific habits related to speaking too, such as tensing our throats and depressing our larynx, but these are also connected with our overall balance and poise.

The vocal mechanism is a sophisticated system combining many different parts including our lungs, vocal chords and the various resonating cavities. In order for it to work efficiently, there needs to be a certain tone in all our muscles. In other words, a similar quality of lengthening and widening of our torso that is necessary for healthy upright poise is also needed for our vocal mechanism to function properly. If we collapse into a slouch, the whole body mechanism is not engaged, just like a violin that has all its strings slackened. They need to be 'tuned up' so that they can vibrate at a required pitch. Conversely, it is also harmful for our torsos to be tensed and held rigid, as that too restricts resonance and sound quality. A distinction needs to be made between essential muscle tone and wasteful tension that can interfere with the quality of our performance. The type of muscle tone needed can only be attained by the efficient working of the whole body; in other words, by means of a free lengthening and widening of our stature.

If we're performing in public, our voice may well need additional support, but that too needs to be achieved through an initially well-functioning body.

It is also essential for us to be able to breathe in and out without collapsing or hollowing our chest and losing our overall height. Our breath is the energy behind our voice, which is created by a free and expansive body. Unfortunately, many of us lose this natural quality with the onset of postural habits and with it we lose the necessary power to produce sound efficiently through our mouths. And if we start to try hard or make an effort, we will only succeed in making unnecessary tensions which will exacerbate the problem. The sound may then be hoarse, strained, thin and lacking resonance. Nor will we be able to sustain it for long periods without difficulty.

A good speaking voice is not just a quirk of nature and a blessing, although it could be seen as such. It is also the product of a physique that is not being misused in a manner that will affect it detrimentally. And while vocal training can do a vast amount to develop a beautiful speaking voice, true success cannot be achieved without paying attention to the physical condition within the body. Without getting into too much detail, we can help ourselves by looking a little bit at how the voice works.

How the voice works

The air from our lungs passes through our larynx where our vocal chords are located. The larynx is suspended by various muscles within the neck, which in turn connect to the main framework of our skeleton. Our 'instrument' is tuned up by the lengthening and widening of our body. This toning of our musculature encourages the larynx to be suspended appropriately so that it can function efficiently. The vocal chords in the larynx are in turn stretched and they vibrate as air passes through them to create sound waves. The pitch at which they vibrate is dependent on the amount of stretch within the chords. If they're slack they will vibrate slower and at a lower pitch, and if they're tauter they will vibrate more quickly and at a higher pitch. This is similar to the strings of a violin or guitar. If we are collapsing in stature, this suspensory mechanism will be slackened and it will be difficult to speak well.

So we have air and vibration, but for it all to be heard we need to give it resonance, and that is where our various resonating cavities play their part. These are mostly located in our head, mouth and throat, but our torso also adds lower harmonics if it's allowed to resonate. They all combine to vary the sounds for speech and song. We need to ensure that these cavities are not blocked or deadened and our vocal chords are not interfered with. Similarly, when a town crier's bell is struck, the bell will vibrate and continue to ring until the vibrations eventually subside. However, if we put our hand on the bell after we've struck it, we will deaden the sound. If we tighten our chest, we deaden our sound. If we can allow our chest to be open and expansive without unnecessary tension, then we will have a wide range of harmonics and we may be surprised at how rich and resonant our voice sounds.

If we are stiffening our neck, pulling our head back off balance, and pulling ourselves down in front, we are jamming the system by depressing our larynx so that the vocal chords can't vibrate properly. We will also be preventing the free flow of air from our lungs, as the ribs and diaphragm that make our lungs breathe won't be able to move so easily. If our postural and vocal mechanism isn't working efficiently we may perceive this as a vocal weakness that may cause us to try harder to be heard, but this will bring about hoarseness and strain.

The qualities of a beautiful voice are difficult to describe. Indeed a wide range of types of voice are appealing: some may be soft, warm and mellow, while others are more resonant and gritty, or light and clear; and there are many more. However, there is a combination of qualities that we could work to develop that will have a positive effect on our voice. We could describe these qualities as being clear and articulate, not husky or 'woolly', resonant, warm and rich in tone with a variety of pitch. A voice displaying these qualities could be described as having 'liquid bite'. We are all individuals with our own size, shape and characteristics that will influence the sound we make. We will inevitably have a voice that is different from anyone else, and we should be proud of it. But we may enjoy becoming more observant of our voice and we can all do a little work on it to enhance certain qualities and to make it the most beautiful and effective voice possible.

One of Britain's leading sports TV commentators came for sessions some time ago on the recommendation of his voice coach. He had been struggling and straining to reach some of the high notes in speech that are so important in sports commentating to convey the excitement of the occasion. As always, I chose not to work with him on voice initially, but we turned our attention to his manner of standing, sitting and the way that he held himself in normal day-to-day life.

We worked on releasing unnecessary tensions and bringing him into balance, as he had the tendency to lean forwards and consequently tighten his knees, calves and back. Becoming more upright allowed the lengthening and widening necessary for healthy poise, which in turn helped free up his breathing. The tightness in his throat and around his chest began to release and he opened out across his shoulders, expanding in stature. These changes brought about a real improvement in his voice; it became richer, with more texture, resonance and what I can only describe as a 'liquid bite'. We experimented in varying pitch from highs to lows without losing his now tall, broad stature and he produced a much wider vocal range with beautiful richness. It hadn't been the power that he lacked but the quality. He now says that he's benefited more from these sessions than he ever did with his voice coach, and feels that the Alexander Technique can be of immense help to anyone involved in public speaking.

Improving your voice

To have an effective speaking voice, it is necessary to breathe freely and effortlessly, and I would refer you to chapter 6 for more details on this important aspect.

Let's do a couple of exercises that will help produce more resonance in our voice.

Exercise: Humming and resonance

This is an exercise of humming through closed lips but will be developed into a more open sound later. As always it will be helpful to ensure that your poise is as upright and free as possible to allow your vocal mechanism to function well. Bring yourself up to your full stature, free your neck, shoulders and back. Remain upright and endeavour to be relaxed.

---

1. Free your neck by allowing your nose to drop slightly.
2. Allow your head to 'teeter' on top of your spine. Think of lengthening and widening.
3. Let your tongue lie relaxed on the floor of your mouth with the tip of it just behind your lower teeth.

Now we will hum.

4. Choose a note that is in your mid range to hum through closed lips.
5. Do not purse your lips. Just allow them to touch each other lightly.
6. Listen to your sound and detect whether it is husky, breathy, or tight-sounding.
7. Allow your lips and cheeks to vibrate freely. You may even sense them quiver.
8. Work on your sound and experiment with using the minimum of air, so that it doesn't come out excessively through your nose and at the same volume. The sound should be clear, free, pure and resonant.
9. Choose a slightly lower note and sense the resonant vibrations in your chest.
10. Choose a higher note and sense the vibrations higher in your head.

Ensure that you do not force the sound, and stop before you run out of breath. Make your hums last for three to four seconds. Don't reach too high or too low. Use your comfortable vocal range.

Practise regularly.

After the above exercise to help improve your resonance, you will benefit from the following exercise, vocalising to make an ahh with your mouth open. The key is to remain free of tension and upright all the time and minimise the effort you make.

Exercise: Vocalised ahh

Let's do the same exercise starting with a hum then opening our mouth halfway through the hum so that it becomes an 'Ahh'.

1. Bring yourself up to your full stature and free your neck, shoulders and back. Remain upright and relaxed.
2. Free your neck by allowing your nose to drop slightly.
3. Allow your head to 'teeter' on top of your spine, think of your head going forwards and up, and of your back lengthening and widening.
4. Place the tip of your relaxed tongue behind your lower teeth.
5. Now perform the hum at a comfortable pitch but allow your mouth to open after one second. Don't stretch your mouth or use any effort. Just allow your jaw to drop – and smile!
6. Make a round open shape inside your mouth and leave your throat open.
7. Listen to the sound you make. Encourage the same resonance and 'liquid bite' that we had during the hum.
8. Endeavour to avoid huskiness or any tightness. Look for richness, clarity and pureness of sound.
9. Try higher notes and then lower notes without straining.

Once you have a good, resonating sound, all you have to do is articulate it. This is achieved by a combination of the shape of your mouth, and the use of your tongue, lips and teeth. Many people do not use their mouth fully and so their words can come out as a mumble. When the speaker isn't being heard well and is asked to speak up, they can make the mistake of just trying to speak louder. What may actually be required is more resonance to the voice in all the high and low harmonics (see exercises above), as well as better articulation. If you listen to a French person speaking, you will notice that there is a wide range of sounds coming from their mouth. And if you look at them as they speak you will see a full movement of the lips, tongue and shape of their whole mouth. Speaking French demands this.

Next time you're watching TV look out for the UK presenter Trevor McDonald and listen to his beautifully articulated and clear voice and notice the generous movement of his mouth. When the words are shaped well in this way, and there is a good range of resonating harmonics, then the speaker can talk quite quietly and the sound will be easily heard some distance away. This technique is used by stage actors so that they can whisper on stage and the audience at the back of the balcony will still be able to hear what they're saying.

Exercise: Articulation

When you are speaking normally, try to articulate your words so that they have consonants at both the beginning of the word and also at the end. It's very easy for us to drop the 't' and other

---

consonants so that our words are just a series of vowels. By enhancing your consonants, your voice will be clearer and more easily heard from a distance without raising your voice. As with everything in this book, use as little effort as you can when speaking and allow your neck to be free and your lips and tongue to be relaxed. It will all work beautifully well without making a huge effort.

A clear, resonating voice that is well articulated and not rushed can be a very useful tool in any business situation, presentation and negotiation. A good voice can denote high calibre, a solid business demeanour, confidence and reassurance. These qualities can only be achieved if you have good natural poise, and avoid tensing your throat, stiffening generally and shortening your stature.

Roger is merchandise director for a menswear retail clothing company. He is required to make presentations to his board on proposed range planning but finds the process very difficult. The whole experience makes him distinctly uncomfortable, nervous, and during his talk his voice is weak and husky so he's not easily heard. Roger explained that he would like to come across more effectively. When I met him it was clear that his manner of holding himself was harmful and it wasn't surprising that he felt a certain inadequacy. However, he hadn't realised until I told him that it wasn't 'him' per se that was the problem, but the way in which he 'used himself' to speak.

From the experience of our sessions, he practised maintaining upright poise with a freer neck. His sense of confidence improved with the refinement of his balance and breathing, and his voice became more resonant as he released the tensions around his chest. He was now looking much more confident and the change in his apparent calibre was quite dramatic.

IN A NUTSHELL

- A beautiful voice can do as much for us as personal grooming and attractive clothing.
- At work, a great voice can do wonders for your career by giving you charisma, power, integrity and gravitas.
- The sound we make is a product of our vocal mechanism. How we use this affects the quality of sound.
- Poor posture, stiffening, slouching and tightening neck muscles will all affect the sound we make.
- In order to make a beautiful sound we need to be free, upright and in balance.

HELPFUL TIPS

1. Practise the guidelines in chapter 6 to help you maintain your full height and natural free poise.
2. Practise Humming and Vocalised ahh exercises
3. Avoid straining when speaking.
4. Good articulation requires a full use of your mouth. Allow your mouth to form the letters fully and with as little effort as possible.

Coping with Major Life Changes

We have looked at many of life's situations and seen how it's possible to enhance our performance and improve our health and wellbeing. There are also times in our lives that are demanding in a different way. Life is full of ups and downs and it will be helpful if we can cope with these in a way that causes us the least amount of strain and harm. First, let's look at one of life's most joyful experiences.

Enjoying pregnancy

One of the most wonderful and exciting moments in our lifetime must be when we get news that we are expecting a baby. It is, and rightly should be, the proudest of moments in our life. Our new, gorgeous offspring will be totally dependent on us for quite some time, and it will be appropriate if the notion crosses our mind that we need to care for ourselves too. If we are to look after a new baby, it's important that we are fit and healthy to do so. Being pregnant puts enormous demands on us physically as well as mentally, and we should take care to avoid putting ourselves under unnecessary strain that may affect the health of our child, our own health or our enjoyment of this time in our life.

Pregnancy is a time when being a biped could be considered as a distinct disadvantage. Yet a woman in pregnancy is the most natural thing in the world, and nature has not done such a bad job over millions of years of evolution as not to provide you with the ability to cope well at such a time. By standing on two feet as you do, however, with a high centre of gravity, there is an enormous potential to become off balance and therefore put considerable strain throughout your supporting framework and musculature. When you carry something you are adding to your own weight and this extra burden can potentially be quite harmful unless you take care.

Coping with the extra weight

We have been discussing the effects of postural habits and how they affect us in our daily life. These habits will have changed our co-ordination and posture so we are probably already under strain. Most of us are using extra effort throughout our body to prevent ourselves from falling over but we're not aware of these habits because they've been with us for such a long time. Now, if you are pregnant, you will realise that your unborn child is adding considerable weight to your body in a relatively short period of time. And as you are a biped standing on only two feet, you can see that it would be easy for you to become unstable.

Although you will gain weight generally over your whole body during pregnancy, your growing baby's weight is located in one place. With this weight positioned where it is, if you're not careful you may compensate by leaning backwards from the waist. But the imbalance doesn't stop there and you may also jut your neck and head forwards. The overall effect is that you fight the gravitational pull because you're so off balance and consequently stiffen quite harmfully.

However, if we were to stand as nature would have us, free of habit, we can enjoy healthy poise by allowing our whole body weight to be more vertically aligned over our ankles so that we are upright and not leaning or arching our back. We will then be more likely to retain a tall posture without strain. See chapter 6, Balancing with a weight exercise.

If you've got the habit of slouching, it will be beneficial both to yourself and your unborn child if you can maintain an upright posture that allows the maximum internal space. Slouching compresses your whole insides including your tummy and of course your baby. Follow the guidelines offered throughout this book to help you maintain healthy posture.

Exercise: Crawling

This is helpful for everyone. It is especially good for women in all stages of pregnancy and particularly after thirty-six weeks to encourage the baby to rotate into the appropriate position. It will help improve your co-ordination and also help strengthen your back. The important thing is that the exercise is done accurately and not haphazardly.

Take your time.

1. Go down on to the floor on to your hands and knees. Your

---

face should be looking at the floor and not ahead of you, as doing so would make you pull your head backwards and stiffen your neck.

2. Space your knees so that they are aligned under your hips.

3. Place your hands palms down, spaced apart under your shoulders and with your fingers pointing forwards.

4. You should feel rather like a table with a flat straight back, your hands under your shoulders and your knees under your hips.

5. Rock slowly and gently backwards and forwards. The crown of your head leads the way forwards, then think of your bottom leading the way backwards. Think of your back lengthening as you rock. Do this a few times before crawling forwards.

6. When you want to crawl forwards, rock forward, *leading with your head*, and move your left knee forwards 9 inches. Follow this by moving your left hand forwards by the same amount. Then move your right knee by 9 inches then your right hand by the same amount. Think of leading with your head. Now repeat the sequence to move forwards: knee, hand, knee, hand, knee, etc.

7. Each short 'step' should be made rhythmically like the regular tick of a clock. Do not rush. Think of leading with the crown of your head and your back lengthening as you do this exercise.

This exercise can also be performed using diagonal opposite hands and knees, i.e. left knee followed by right hand, then right knee followed by left hand.

Lifting and carrying children

As with any heavy item that we want to lift from the floor, it's important that we bend from our knees and hips while keeping our back tall and broad. Get as close as you can so that you're not leaning too much. Put one foot slightly in front of the other in a 'lunge' type of pose to help your balance and stability, then bend your knees as you go down so that you go into a type of squat. Keep your chest broad and bring the child close to you facing your chest. All the time keep your thoughts of your head going upwards and then lead with your head as you come back up to standing to encourage your back to lengthen. If you're picking up a child from a cot or pram, get as close as you can and go into a 'lunge' type of position with your front leg and your own body as close to her as possible to avoid leaning and straining your back. See chapter 6 for more details.

When you are carrying young children, hold them close to your chest with one arm round them and the other underneath. This is the closest you can get to the natural situation during pregnancy. If you carry your child on your hip, it is likely to cause your spine to twist and put strain on your lower back. If you are carrying a baby for any length of time you may find it helpful to use a sling. This may have the tendency to pull you forwards so it's important to keep your weight back from your ankles and keep 'thinking up' with your head. If the child is older, then a back carrier with padded shoulder straps and waist strap will help. These items are properly made to ensure that they are comfortable for both parent and child, while also being safe. Again ensure that you are upright and not compensating by leaning from the waist. Keep your thoughts going upwards.

Jamie started having sessions with me a year after she gave birth to her son and explained during our initial chat that she had experienced the most dreadful backache during her pregnancy. She had just recently had confirmation of her second pregnancy and wanted to do everything possible to ensure that she didn't suffer in the same way again. On looking at her, I could see that she tended to stick her tummy out a bit and leaned backwards from the waist and hips. This was also accompanied by a stoop and her neck and head jutted forwards. In some respects the casual onlooker would say that she was quite a relaxed person, but from a postural point of view it was clear that her body was under strain. When her baby grows larger, the added weight in front would throw her more off balance and cause greater strain and probably pain.

We had to work on her whole postural condition and balance rather than any isolated symptom in order to avoid backache during pregnancy. When I guided Jamie into a more upright poise so that she didn't stick her tummy and hips forwards, the experience was so unusual for her that she felt that she was now sticking her bottom out. However this was only in comparison to how she normally stood. Looking side-on in the mirror she could see that this wasn't the case and her feelings were an illusion. She gradually became upright and the new poise became more familiar. We encouraged her head to go upwards and a lengthening and widening of her back by her learning to think correctly. I encouraged Jamie to practise freeing her ankles so that when carrying something she was able to compensate with her whole body and not arch her waist. This would be important during later pregnancy to avoid strain. After the initial course, Jamie had less frequent sessions and eventually completed her pregnancy without any back pain whatsoever.

Infertility and conception

Stress is a well-known contributing factor to our inability to conceive. What is not so commonly understood is how the condition of our body can affect us. Poor posture has a great influence on our wellbeing and the habitual excessive tensions that we can develop throughout our lives can affect us in many ways; infertility can be a symptom for some of us. If we are off balance, tensing our muscles unnecessarily and not breathing well we are physically under strain and also creating a condition in our body where we are likely to feel emotionally stressed. If we are constantly slouching and stooping then the increased pressure on the abdomen doesn't help our circulation and reproductive abilities either. I've worked with a number of women who have found that after a long period of not being able to conceive, they have become pregnant soon after starting sessions in the Alexander Technique. An improvement in our co-ordination and physical wellbeing can be of enormous help.

IN A NUTSHELL

- Good balance is necessary to ensure that you're not under excessive strain.
- The growing weight of your unborn child can cause you to compensate badly unless care is taken to ensure that you are in balance.
- Good posture will help to ensure that you are at your healthiest to conceive and avoid strain and stress during pregnancy.

HELPFUL TIPS

1. When standing, ensure that you *do not* push your hips forwards or lean backwards from your waist. Ensure that you think tall to help you remain upright.

2. It would be beneficial to practise improving your posture *in advance* of becoming pregnant so that you are already in good condition. It is far harder to relieve backache once you're carrying extra weight.

3. Avoid slouching or stooping as this compresses your abdomen. This is particularly important if you are trying to conceive, or during pregnancy.

4. When lifting children, get as close to them as possible and bend your knees, keeping your back tall.

5. When carrying babies or young children, keep them close to you and use a properly made sling or carrier to make it comfortable for longer periods of time.

COPING WITH TRAUMAS

While there are wonderful times during our lives such as having babies and bringing them up in the world, there are also times that are not so joyful. Things go wrong and don't work out as planned such as a relationship breaking down or we have to cope with bereavement. Sometimes it can all feel just too much and overwhelming. We can feel pressured to the point that it's difficult to cope.

Sometimes it seems there's only one thing to do, and that's throw a brick. And there are times when we need to shout and scream to the rooftops, the treetops and into the pillow. If you are going to throw a brick, however, make it a really good heavy one and send it as far as you can; just make sure that you don't hit anyone or cause damage to property that's not your own! But, by God, it's good to throw it! Do it again if you feel like it. Throw a hundred. You can punch or throw a cushion as a safe alternative.

Life seems full of ups and downs, and when it's going down, we can sometimes feel that *everything* is going down, down, down and it's hard to remember when it ever went up. Fortunately whole trains of cataclysmic events don't happen to us very often. But we do experience one-off, major events such as the death of a loved one, divorce or separation, physical trauma or an accident. Such events can have a traumatic impact on us to the point that we feel that our whole life has changed. With the loss of a loved one or other such event we may grieve for some period then try to get back to normal life the best way we can. In some instances it may be beneficial to have professional help in the form of counselling. Physical disability and serious injury can require a long period of convalescence and we may remain physically impaired. Even when the healing is complete, our life may never be the same again.

We experience such major life events not just on one level, such as physical or emotional, but on all levels. Emotional hurt or sadness affects us physically, and physical injury affects us emotionally. Such emotions as anger, stress, fear and resentment can make us stiffen up physically, affecting not only our posture but also our internal functioning, while sadness and depression may cause us to collapse and curl up in a ball. The loss of an arm or leg may make us resentful and bitter. And although healing may eventually be considered complete on one level it may not be the case on the other. Long after the main period of suffering, we can still be hanging on to secondary symptoms, which can cause us serious problems in the long term.

We need to let out our emotions and also to express ourselves physically. If we have suffered the loss of a loved one, it is important that we allow ourselves time to grieve and express our emotions fully. Being 'brave' and smothering our emotions can often lead to difficulties later, such as digestive, bowel problems and even disease. Separation and divorce are an enormous source of stress and again it is necessary to let out our emotions. If we don't give our inner voice that opportunity to be heard, it will continue to nag away inside us, bursting at the gate until we give it the audience it so desperately wants, or it will express itself in a different form and manifest sickness. When we truly let out our emotions and allow our inner voice to speak we will be able to move on.

We can help release held emotions by expressing ourselves

in different ways. We can take time and write it all down, we can talk to someone, scream or write a poem, do a drawing, or dance, act, sing or just jump around.

Razz, a handsome 6 foot 3 inch tanned Californian, is an expert water-skier and was involved in a horrific accident that resulted in his pelvis being broken and one arm having to be amputated.

He went on to have thirteen operations and lost 43 pounds in weight. His wounds eventually healed and he went through occupational rehabilitation and taught himself to write with his left hand. He went back to playing drums in a live band with the help of an artificial arm.

Razz came to terms with his injuries as best he could but felt that there was something still wrong. His therapy had dealt with the physical injury but not his emotions. He was bitter, angry, resentful and sad at losing his arm. His sleeping patterns were also disturbed because he couldn't get comfortable.

Twelve years later in 1980 Razz attended a personal development seminar that was to change his life. During the course each individual was encouraged to express themselves to the full. When the course facilitator asked, 'What do you really want, Razz?' he said clearly that he wanted just to scream. So he did. Razz screamed with all his pent-up anger and rage for several minutes until he passed out. The assistants brought him round with damp towels. He screamed again until he passed out unconscious once more. This continued for a full fifteen minutes, then his screaming subsided and he started to laugh, and he carried on laughing. Later he described his experience as being one of extreme joy and happiness; of freedom and trans-

formation. He had stepped out of his whole situation and was free. Razz says that all the trauma in the cellular memory of his body was released in those moments.

He eventually went on to train as a seminar facilitator in the field of personal development so that he could help others. Thirty-five years after his accident, Razz also does consulting and training seminar design for businesses, the private sector and US Aerospace.

We can help ourselves cope emotionally in difficult situations by ensuring that we are in the best condition possible. For instance physical activity can be a good antidote to bottled-up emotions. Just getting the body moving can help, and physical exertion creates chemical changes that can also help clear blocked and pent-up feelings. Some people find running or swimming helpful in this way. If we've got a job that's rather sedentary and cerebral, then it will be good for us to balance our lives with something physical during our leisure time.

Being emotionally centred

By improving our balance, co-ordination and posture we also become more emotionally centred. When we are more centred, problems, traumatic and difficult situations such as divorce or bereavement affect us less. This doesn't diminish our sense of loss or our love, but we can cope better with the situation. We can grieve and express ourselves fully over what has happened, but without tearing ourselves apart. Wallowing doesn't help either the person who has left us, or ourselves. Eventually we need to move on. This is not being unfeeling or uncaring. We must express our emotions, as holding on to them is similar to holding on to physical tensions and can become habitual. If we allow our emotions full expression and let go of them, we are helping both physical and emotional healing. The more balanced and centred we are, the better we will be able to express our true feelings without them wrecking our lives. And for us, life goes on. Even if we've lost a limb, life goes on, as Razz has shown us. If you're going to cry, get on with it: really cry. But don't think of your emotions in isolation from your whole body. Attend to your need to be physically balanced and centred to help you be emotionally centred too. Breathe well and release your emotions; then you will be free. When we have fully expressed ourselves and ensured that we are physically loose and well balanced, we will be open to new opportunities.

IN A NUTSHELL

- Our emotional feelings and physical condition cannot be separated.
- Emotional upset can cause physical problems, and personal injury can have emotional side-effects.
- Holding back and bottling up our emotions can cause sickness.
- We can minimise our personal suffering, without necessarily diminishing our love or feelings towards another, by ensuring that our posture and balance are good.

HELPFUL TIPS

1. Allow your emotions full expression. Don't bottle them up.
2. Physical activity is good for unwinding and shifting stress, anger or resentment.
3. By improving your posture, balance and co-ordination you will be able to cope more easily with severe emotional upset.

LONGEVITY

I mentioned earlier that I had an elderly client who was a centenarian. In fact she was 102 years old when I met her at an introductory evening course I was running for the Alexander Technique. Ella was a bright and sprightly lady of 4 feet 11 and a half inches in height and full of the joys of spring. When I asked her why she wanted to have sessions from me, her comment was, 'I don't think my posture is very good, and I am feeling a bit stiff.' Great reasons to come along, I thought, and what an attitude for someone of her great age! When the class finished, she expressed interest in having some one-to-one sessions so we made arrangements to meet.

Ella and I enjoyed weekly sessions together for nearly two years, and during that time I was privileged to hear some of her many stories. I heard about her trips down to Lyons' tearoom in Piccadilly by horse-drawn cab and her travels around the world. Her last major trip was when she was 'only' ninety and had travelled by herself for three months across America by Greyhound bus. 'Wonderful, just absolutely wonderful!' she said when describing her holiday.

She also commented on our sessions: 'I feel taller [her height increased by ½ inch to 5 feet], my breathing is easier, and also being looser helps me maintain my balance in those awful winter winds which previously threatened to blow me over. Now I feel stronger, I hope to be able to carry on for a few more years.' And she did, until she was 104.

On one occasion, I asked Ella why she thought she'd lived so long, as all her family had died, if I recall correctly, between the ages of sixty and seventy-five. She told me that it was her attitude of mind. She never held a grudge or let anger take hold. She was grateful for whatever came her way, and if things didn't work out as she hoped, or if she'd been let down by someone or an event, she would just accept it. That's life. Some things work out and others don't. She told me, 'Everyone is getting angry, and that's what makes them sick.' I asked her if she'd thought this way all her life, and she said, 'Oh no! Only since I was seventy!' Here was a lady who, despite her great age and experience, felt that she might be able to do something to help herself enjoy life a little more, so she started having sessions long after many people would have given up and waited for the bell to ring 'time up'.

Ella commented during one session, 'All my life I've believed that I need to hold myself up like this . . .' [she demonstrated a sergeant major type of stance] and now you show me that I don't need to, and it can be so much easier. That's wonderful! Thank you!' God bless her, she herself was wonderful.

Most of us would like to live as long as Ella provided that we can be healthy and happy, but there are many things that can happen to us. We can all be affected by such things as disease, accident, illness and environmental and social conditions. However, taking aside these sorts of problems, there are other reasons, too, why most of us may not enjoy a good quality of life so far into old age. I'm not talking about financial considerations, family issues, or even our diet, although these can obviously have a huge influence on us. I'm thinking of all the issues that we've talked about throughout this book.

Good poise for healthier old age

As we get older, we become an exaggerated version of the way we were in our youth. Habits of tension and getting off balance are often established when we're young, and with a lifetime's practice become more and more pronounced. Aside from bone loss, for instance, we can shrink in height just because we're stiffening, stooping and hunching with rounded shoulders. We may develop a widow's hump. During most of our lives we are able to hold ourselves up despite being off balance by stiffening. However, in our later years we are no longer strong enough, so we're likely to need a stick or walking frame to lean on. Our habits can deform us terribly so that we are distorted and severely off balance.

Our deteriorating posture puts untold pressures on us. Excessive tensions flatten our spinal discs causing them eventually to dry out and offer reduced cushioning or shock absorption. Nor will they allow free rotation or bending of our spine so we become more rigid and fixed in our worsening contortion. Unnecessary tensions will also compress our hip, knee and ankle joints, so they too become stiff and limited in their range of movement. All these habitual tendencies bring about a reduction in flexibility, and excessive wear and tear on the joints can cause irritation, inflammation and eventually joint disease, possibly leading to the need for a joint replacement operation.

Our tensions will also have an effect on the efficient working of our whole system and impair our general functioning. We may experience deterioration of our digestion because of the pressure we create inside, so heartburn and indigestion become the norm. Bowel movements may become sluggish. We may not breathe adequately because the ribs and diaphragm are not moving freely, resulting in insufficient oxygenation of our body. Poor breathing can contribute to the possibility of all sorts of disorders including inadequate cell growth and even brain disease. Our circulation may be affected as the blood flow is restricted by tension, causing cold hands and feet, but also leads to a build-up of blood pressure and possible heart disease.

Many conditions normally related to getting old, and which tend to be expected, are not necessarily a direct consequence of age itself. Yet we expect them because they happen to most elderly people. As I've said, just because some conditions may be common, that doesn't make them 'natural', and it's possible that if we looked after ourselves a little better during our younger years we could avoid them occurring later.

We should remember that tension is something that we do to ourselves, and not something that is done to us, so to speak. If we are stiff, then it is because we ourselves are doing the stiffening. If I've got a backache, then it is me who is likely to be off balance and stiffening my muscles in such a way as to cause the discomfort. Of course, we must take into account accidents, surgery, or disease that would have an influence. But there are a great number of people who have not had any such afflictions but suffer some sort of discomfort or lack of health and wellbeing because they are unwittingly doing things within themselves. If we have had an injury or surgery we may be making our condition worse by our self-inflicted postural habits, and to be free of them would perhaps allow us to enjoy a better quality of life despite our limitations.

If we were able to maintain good poise by eliminating our habitual and harmful tendencies, we might even live a little longer, and be far happier and healthier right into our old age.

Help yourself retain youthful poise

There are a number of ways in which you can help avoid unnecessary deterioration and maintain good health into old age. This whole book has been about helping ourselves be healthier, happier and more successful and I recommend that you use these guidelines to enhance your life. Let's recap on some of them.

1. Loosen as much as you can and allow your head to balance freely on top of your spine.
2. Think of your head going upwards and your back lengthening and widening. This will help avoid compression of your internal organs and keep your back strong.
3. Ensure that you're breathing freely by staying free. Avoid holding your breath. Perform the Breathing exercise in chapter 5.

4. Endeavour to be in balance and not leaning forwards when you walk or stand. Being off balance puts enormous strain on your system. Think loose and tall.

IN A NUTSHELL

- It is possible that we are deteriorating and ageing ourselves more quickly than is 'natural'.
- We can help ourselves maintain good health and functioning right into old age by following the principles in this book.
- Free, tall poise helps our body function better and helps us cope better in later years.

HELPFUL TIPS

1. Let go of anger.
2. Try not to hold a grudge or ill feeling.
3. Improve your posture now to avoid unnecessary deterioration.
4. To help you enjoy better health and mobility right into old age, use the principles of the Alexander Technique.

Poise for Life

Good poise is fundamental to our overall health and our ability to achieve our full potential in life. It affects everything we do. But although it is our birthright, we begin to lose this quality from the age of three or four. We all have the natural instinct for healthy poise from birth and it remains with us throughout our whole life; it just needs to be revived. You can begin to revive your own natural poise now, by consciously eliminating harmful postural habits.

It's not possible to 'do' good poise and you can't 'do' good health, but you can encourage and 'allow' it to happen. If you stop the wrong things, the right thing will look after itself. Your body's tendency is towards health and wellbeing. It is by and large self-healing and if you create the right environment where unwanted strain and harmful conditions are removed, your body will be better able to restore itself to health and vitality.

It is my belief that we can all change and improve our lives and even excel beyond our expectations. We can improve our health, our sense of wellbeing, how we interact with others, and allow our full natural beauty and potential to be expressed.

We can perform better at any activity we undertake. Changing your poise can enhance every aspect of your life. And the person in control of your life is you – no one else. It is for you to make your choices.

Improving your poise brings with it a natural confidence – a real confidence. You develop the strength and belief in yourself to do what you *want* to do and not just what you *have* to do. You can choose how you want to be and how you want to perform. You can choose to change your life, or you can choose to leave it mainly as it is and enhance certain aspects that are not quite ideal.

Even if you believe that you're already doing well, it's probable that you could make refinements and improvements to many aspects of your life by using the principles of the Alexander Technique outlined in this book.

It starts where we began, as children with an instinct for poise that provides the ability to excel at virtually anything you do. Rediscover this dormant instinct by removing some engrained habits. Give your life a kick-start and watch how you can change if you wish, in almost every endeavour and every way. If you revive your natural poise it will help change your life. It has done so for me, and it can for you too. The choice is there for you to take, and should you do so, you may be surprised at just how wonderful you truly are, and how great your life can be.

Useful Addresses

Alexander Technique

To find a local teacher of the Alexander Technique, contact the appropriate society from the list below.

Australia
Australian Society of Teachers of the Alexander Technique (AUSTAT)
Po Box 716, Darlinghurst, NSW 2010, Australia
Tel: +61 2 9247 5991
1800 339 571 Free call within Australia
Website: www.alexandertechnique.org.au
e-mail: info@alexandertechnique.org.au

Belgium
Belgian Association of Teachers of F.M. Alexander Technique (AEFMAT)
408, Brusselstrat, 1702 Groot Bijgaarden, Belgium
Tel: +32 2 245 8235
Website: www.fmalexandertech.be
e-mail: aefmat.secretary@fmalexandertech.be

Brazil
Associação Brazileira da Técnica Alexander (ABTA)
Caixa Postal 16020, Rio de Janeiro, RJ Brasil, CEP
22220–970
Tel: +55 21 239 66 18 Fax: +55 21 239 66 18
Website: www.abtalexander.com.br
e-mail: abta@abtalexander.com.br

Canada
**Canadian Society of Teachers of the Alexander Technique
(CANSTAT)**
RPO 984 West Broadway, PO Box 53568, Vancouver, BC,
Canada V52 1KO
Tel: +1 416 631 8127 Fax: +1 416 631 0094
Website: www.canstat.ca
e-mail: canstat@istar.ca

Denmark
**Danish Society of Teachers of the Alexander Technique
(DFLAT)**
c/o Hultberg, Laessøesgade, 2200 COPENHAGEN N.
Tel: +45 7025 5070
Website: www.dflat.dk
e-mail: info@dflat.dk

France
**Association Française des Professeurs de la Technique
Alexander (APTA)**
42 Terrace de l'Iris, La Défence 2, 92400
Courbevoie, France

Tel: +33 1 40 90 0623 Fax: +33 1 40 90 0623
Website: www.techniquealexander.info
e-mail: techniquealexander@yahoo.fr

Germany
German Society of Teachers of the Alexander Technique (GLAT)
Postfach 5312, 79020 Freiburg, Germany
Tel: +49 761 383 357 Fax: +49 761 383 357
Website: www.alexander-technik.org
e-mail: glat-freiburg@t-online.de

Israel
Israeli Society of Teachers of the Alexander Technique (ISTAT)
PO Box 16163, Tel Aviv 61161, Israel
Tel: +972 3 522 7979
e-mail: gal@alexanderisrael.org
Website: www.alexanderisrael.org.ai

Netherlands
Netherlands Society of Teachers of the Alexander Technique (NeVLAT)
Postbus 15591, 1001 NB Amsterdam, Netherlands
Tel: +31 20 625 3163
Website: www.alexandertechniek.nl
e-mail: info@alexandertechniek.nl

New Zealand
Alexander Technique Teachers Society New Zealand (ATTSNZ)
PO Box 3020, Wellington, New Zealand
Website: www.alexandertechnique.org.nz
e-mail: info@alexandertechnique.org.nz

South Africa
The South African Society of Teachers of the Alexander Technique (SASTAT)
PO Box 30629
Tokai 7966
South Africa
Tel: +27 72 845 6138
Website: www.alexandertechnique.org.za
e-mail: atteachers@iafrica.com

Spain
Asociacion de Profesores de la Tecnica Alexander de Espana (APTAE)
Apartado 156, 28080 Madrid, Spain
Tel: +34 637 2483 43
Website: www.aptae.net
e-mail: info@aptae.net

Switzerland
Schweizerischer Verband der Lehrerinnen und Lehrer der F.M. Alexander-Technik (SVLAT)
Postfach 8032 Zurich, Switzerland
Tel: +41 1 201 0343

Website: www.alexandertechnik.ch
e-mail: info@svlat.ch

United Kingdom
The Society of Teachers of the Alexander Technique (STAT)
Linton House, 39–51 Highgate Road, London NW5 1RS, United Kingdom
Tel: +44 (0)845 230 7828 Fax: +44 (0)20 7482 5435
Website: www.stat.org.uk for a list of teachers in the UK
e-mail: enquiries@stat.org.uk

USA
The American Society for the Alexander Technique (AmSAT)
30 North Maple, PO Box 60008, Florence, MA 01062 USA
Tel: +1 413 584 2359 Fax: +1 413 584 3097
Toll free within USA (800) 473 0620
Website: www.amsat.ws
e-mail: info@amsat.ws

Shaw Method of Swimming
Based on the Alexander Technique
27 Greenway Close, London N20 8ES, United Kingdom
Tel: 020 8446 9442
Website: www.artofswimming.com
e-mail: info@artofswimming.com

Personal Development

Insight Seminars
2101 Wilshire Boulevard, Suite 101, Santa Monica, CA
90292 USA
Tel: (310) 315-9733
Website: www.insightseminars.org

Insight Seminars UK
62A Kempshott Road
London
SW16 5LH
Tel: +44 (0)208 679 4215
Website: www.insightuk.org
e-mail: fiona@insightuk.org

Noël Kingsley, MSTAT
21 Harcourt House, 19 Cavendish Square, London W1G 0PL
Tel: +44(0)20 7491 3505
Website: www.alexander-technique.com
e-mail: noel@alexander-technique.com

The Essence Foundation
5 Birchwood Avenue, London N10 3BE, United Kingdom
Tel: +44 (0)20 8883 2888
Website: www.essence-foundation.com
e-mail: enquiry@essence-foundation.com